the Forth
Naturalist
*and*Historian

Volume 19

Published by the Forth Naturalist and Historian, University of Stirling – an approved charity and member of the Scottish Publishers Association. 1996.

ISSN 0309-7560

ISBN 1 898008 12 4

Supported by BP in Scotland.

Cover: front– Heart of Scotland's Environment (HSE) – CD-Rom Menu
        (SCET)
        back– Clackmannanshire (D. Grinly)

Printed by Meigle Printers Ltd., Tweedbank Industrial Estate, Galashiels.
Set in Zapf Calligraphic on 90gsm Fyneprint and white gloss cover.

CLACKMANNANSHIRE LANDSCAPE AND GEOLOGY

Mike Browne (BGS) and David Grinly

The name Clackmannan is derived from the Stone (Clack) of Mannan which stands with the Mercat Cross and Tolbooth at the centre of the town. This account of the Wee County's geology is freely based on the Forth Naturalist and Historian's book *Central Scotland – land, wildlife, people* (1993).

LANDSCAPE AND GEOLOGY

The landscape of Clackmannanshire generally reflects the weathering characteristics of the bedrock, being upstanding where underlain by harder, mainly igneous rocks and low-lying where underlain by softer rocks such as mudstones and many sandstones. The view of Clackmannanshire from the National Wallace Monument highlights three distinct landscapes (photo below and back cover): – the steep scarp and high hills of the Ochils running eastwards through Menstrie and Dollar; the lowlying floors of the Devon and Forth valleys; and the rounded low hilly ground of the Clackmannan 'Ridge'. This tripartite division is also reflected in the generalized soil type map of the county (Figure 1). The classification used in this figure is based on that of Taylor and Nortcliff (1996, p.9). The Ochil Fault contributes a marked linear scarp feature to the landscape where it has brought hard rocks against soft. The scarp has slope gradients as high as 1 in 1.5 between 15m OD and 500m OD Summits in the Ochils (Figure 2) have an average height of about 2150ft/650m OD with the highest Ben Cleuch 2363ft/721m. By contrast, the highest point on the Clackmannan 'Ridge' is only about 400ft/120m (Figure 3).

The igneous and sedimentary rocks seen in the County are between 410 and 290 million years old. The geological map (Figure 4) shows the distribution of these rocks. They fall into two main suites with the older Lower Devonian volcanic rocks to the north of the Ochil Fault and the younger mainly Carboniferous sedimentary rocks to the south. The succession is divided into

D. Grinly

Ochils – Devon and Forth floors/windings – distant Clackmannan.

formations and groups according to their lithological characteristics and these subdivisions are shown in stratigraphical order in Table 1.

Table 1. Lithostratigraphical Succession in Clackmannanshire

Quaternary		Grangemouth Formation
		Claret Formation
		Letham Formation
		Bothkennar Gravel Formation
		Abbotsgrange/Linwood formations
		Killearn Formation
		Kinneil Kerse Formation
		Loanhead Formation
		Broomhouse Formation
		Wilderness Till Formation
Carboniferous	Coal Measures	Middle Coal Measures
		Lower Coal Measures
	Clackmannan Group	Passage Formation
		Upper Limestone Formation
		Limestone Coal Formation
		Lower Limestone Formation
	Strathclyde Group	Lawmuir Formation
		Kirkwood Formation
		Clyde Plateau Volcanic Formation
	Inverclyde Group	Clyde Sandstone Formation
		Ballagan Formation
		Kinnesswood Formation
Upper Devonian	Stratheden Group	Knox Pulpit Formation
		Stockiemuir/Glenvale Formation/
		Burnside Formation
Lower Devonian	Arbuthnott Group	Ochil Volcanic Formation

Formations shown in bold italics are unknown from outcrop or borehole records, but are surmised to be present under Clackmannanshire.

Rocks of Devonian age (410-360 million years ago) – Table 1 and Figure 4

During the Devonian, Scotland was located south of the equator, having 'drifted' northwards from the southern polar latitudes which it had occupied in Precambrian times (>570 million years ago). The climate was hot and seasonally wet, with limited rainfall.

The oldest rocks cropping out in the County are of the Ochil Volcanic Formation in the Ochil Hills. The formation comprises over 2000m of subaerial basaltic and andesitic lava flows with interbedded terrestrial debris-flow conglomerates. In the upper part of the volcanic sequence there are more acidic flows of trachyandesite as seen on Craig Leith (OS 58, NS 875 980). Differential weathering of the bedding within the lava flows and volcaniclastic conglomerates, accentuated by severe glacial erosion during the ice ages of the last two million years, produced the step-like (trap) featuring of the prominent ridges on the scarp face of the Ochils. The flows are sometimes fresh, compact and columnar jointed, but more often are autobrecciated (blocky lava), or generally weathered and decomposed. Only a small proportion of airfall and waterlain volcanic ashes appears to be present in the succession.

The lava flows are often porphyritic mainly with small (1-3mm) white or grey crystals of feldspar in a fine-grained matrix. Altered small crystals (1-2mm) of olivine preserved as the red mineral iddingsite also occur. Flows with vesicles (gas cavities) are also common. Often the vesicles are filled, or partly filled with minerals such as calcite and quartz to form amygdales or geodes containing agate and amethyst etc. Commonly the amygdales and geodes weather out of the parent rock and can be recognised in soil or scree (eg. between Blairlogie and Menstrie) by the toad-skin appearance of the dimpled indented outer surface. Sometimes the outer skin is green in colour due to the presence of epidote or chlorite rather than of copper in the form of malachite as is often assumed.

The main vents, or the eroded roots of the andean-like volcanoes from which the flows were erupted have not yet been located and may lay deeply buried under the younger rocks preserved to the south of the Ochil Fault. Contrary to local opinion based on its cone-like landform, Dumyat (just in Stirlingshire) is not an extinct volcano. The only possible, small volcanic neck so far recognised is now under water in the Upper Glendevon Reservoir (NN 907 046).

The volcanic terrain of the Ochils formed part of the southern margin of a major subsiding sedimentary basin located in Strathmore to the north of the County. In this basin, large volumes of detritus, from the Caledonian mountains to the north, were moved in large river systems towards the sea, the then coastline being located in north Wales. Erosion of the volcanic terrane provided an input of sediment northwards to these rivers.

Several types of intrusive igneous rock are found in the Ochils that are of a similar age to the volcanic succession. At Tillicoultry, a coarse-grained diorite stock is found on the east bank of the Mill Glen (NS 920 980) opposite the highly visible scar of the working hardrock quarry of Castle Craigs. The largest stock is found on Elistoun Hill (NS 926 990). The contacts are subvertical between these stocks and the thermally metamorphosed and much indurated rocks of the Ochil Volcanic Formation into which they are intruded. There are also narrow and short dykes of porphyrite and acid porphyrite trending NNW, ENE and E.

In central Scotland the Upper Devonian Stratheden Group, locally up to 1000m thick, was laid down unconformably on an eroded surface of folded Lower Devonian rocks including the Ochil Volcanic Formation. There is no evidence of any rocks of Middle Devonian age. Thus the unconformity represents a considerable interval of time during which tectonic uplift, faulting, folding, and erosion of the Lower Devonian rocks took place.

The mainly fluvial sandstones of the Stratheden Group are known to crop out in the adjacent areas of Stirling (Stockiemuir Sandstone Formation) and

Fife (Burnside, Glenvale formations). These rocks do not crop out in the County but are likely to be found at depth. At the top of the Devonian succession aeolian sandstones become interbedded with or replace the fluvial rocks. These strata of the Knox Pulpit Formation (c.130m thick in Fife) indicate that Scotland, though still south of the equator, had 'drifted' into a desert belt broadly similar to the present day Kalahari desert. These aeolian deposits, though not exposed, are known to exist in the far east of the County.

The sedimentary rocks of the Devonian period in Clackmannanshire contain no fossils, although some of primitive fish are recorded not far away at Wolf's Hole Quarry, Bridge of Allan (OS 57, NS 790 981). The paucity of fossil evidence elsewhere in Scotland makes definition of the junction between rocks of Devonian and Carboniferous age uncertain.

Rocks of Carboniferous age (360-300m years ago) – Table 1 and Figure 4

The oldest Carboniferous strata record a transition from the terrestrial environments of the Devonian to the marine or coastal environments which prevailed during most of this time period.

Inverclyde Group rocks are well exposed in the River Devon and its tributaries around Muckhart Mill (OS 58, NS 993 986) in the east of the County. At the base of the Inverclyde Group is the Kinnesswood Formation, about 150m thick. It consists mainly of fluvial sandstones containing nodules of limestone. These limestone masses, called cornstones, are formed by rapid evaporation pulling salts into the soil layer where they precipitate to form the nodules. The presence of cornstones indicate a semi-arid climate, a mature landscape with periods of tectonic quiescence and reduced rates of sedimentary basin subsidence.

The Kinnesswood Formation is overlain by the coastal lagoonal sedimentary rocks of the Ballagan Formation. This unit consists mainly of mudstone with thin beds of muddy limestone, ferroan dolomite (cementstone) and nodular gypsum/anhydrite (sabkha evaporites). The formation, up to 200 m thick, records the continuing environmental change from the semi-arid terrestrial environments of Devonian times to the tropical coastal marine environments of later Carboniferous times.

The Clyde Sandstone Formation, about 100m thick, consists largely of calcareous sandstones. They are fluvial in origin with conglomerates containing cementstone clasts and algal bodies. Uplift and erosion of part of the early Carboniferous basin may have provided the source of the sediments.

The oldest rocks in the Strathclyde Group are the Clyde Plateau Volcanic Formation; a large pile of lavas, up to 1000 m thick, which extends throughout much of central Scotland. The lavas are mostly basalts and were erupted from large, low-profile volcanoes, small cones and from fissures as in Iceland today. Pyroclastic tuffs, the product of volcanic ash falls, also occur within the sequence. The existence of this formation in Clackmannanshire is surmise (Table 1 and Figure 4).

The Kirkwood Formation consists of reworked volcanic detritus immediately overlying the Clyde Plateau Volcanic Formation. Elsewhere, this formation is up to 60m thick. As a reworked volcanic deposit, it could be present at depth under the County even if the underlying lavas are not. It is surmised that the formation may have been encountered at the bottom of the Inch of Ferryton Oilwell (and see p.15).

During the rest of Carboniferous time, Clackmannanshire may be envisaged as a small part of an extensive low-relief continental margin with a pattern of sedimentation comprising a series of depositional cycles. The cycle may be repeated many times in each formation although it may not be complete: with one or more rock types not represented. A single ideal cycle is illustrated in Figure 5 and by Browne and Mendum (1995, figure on p.13).

The sedimentary cycles of deposition are normally about 5 to 10m thick but can be over 30m. Variations in the thickness, and in the extent to which different rock types occur, give a characteristic pattern of cycles to each formation into which the Carboniferous sequence is divided. The repetition of cycles is, in part, controlled by the migration of deltas and river channels in a generally subsiding basin as well as changes in world sea-levels and by regional earth movements. The rate of compaction of soft sediments is also a factor. At times, conditions were particularly favourable to the growth of lush, tropical to boreal vegetation. The death and partial decay of these forests produced extensive coastal peat bogs now represented by the numerous coal seams in parts of the succession.

The Lawmuir Formation at the top of the Strathclyde Group, known only from borehole records, consists of mudstones, siltstones, sandstones and rare thin limestone beds. The succession is a transitional one between terrestrial and marine conditions and represents the first elements of a marine transgression onto a major land area, elsewhere in part, formed by rocks of the Clyde Plateau Volcanic Formation. Because of faulting the thickness of this formation is unknown.

At the base of the Clackmannan Group is the Lower Limestone Formation. It is 100 to 200m thick and consists of sandstones, siltstones, mudstones and several fossiliferous marine limestones. These sedimentary rocks were deposited in a shallow sea which was regularly silted up as deltas built out seaward. Coal seams are thin and insignificant.

The Limestone Coal Formation is 250 to 500m thick. It consists predominantly of sandstones, siltstones, mudstones and many coals associated with bedded ironstones. These rocks were deposited in cyclic sequence on broad alluvial plains at the terrestrial end of an extending delta. Marine strata form only a minor part of the formation. Neither this unit nor the underlying Lower Limestone Formation are known at surface in the County.

The Upper Limestone Formation consists of deltaic sandstones, siltstones and mudstones with up to seven thin marine limestones. There are a few coals and only the Upper Hirst Coal is known to have been worked to any extent.

The seam is currently mined from the Longannet Mine Complex, Fife but working panels are located to the east of Alloa and to the north of Clackmannan. The formation is between 320 and 500m thick.

The Passage Formation varies considerably in thickness from an average of 270m to only 100m in the east near Dollar. It consists predominantly of sandstones with subordinate poorly bedded siltstones and mudstones (including fireclays), one or two thin impure limestones and calcareous mudstones with marine fossils, and some thin coals. These rocks represent a return to terrestrial, fluvial conditions with occasional short-lived incursions of the sea. Seams of fireclay are present near the base and top of the Passage Formation. Nodular ironstones at the horizon of the No 3 Marine Bed were once worked at Vicar's Bridge near Dollar for the local Forth Ironworks. During the deposition of this formation, uplift of the area may have occurred leading to breaks in the sedimentation such that the base of the formation is locally marked by an unconformity.

The Coal Measures are represented by two, generally non-marine, formations that are not shown separately in Figures 4 and 6. The Lower Coal Measures (100 to 150m thick) consist of sandstones, siltstones, mudstones and seatearth with coals, deposited on broad alluvial plains at the landward end of a delta. At least nine coals in the Lower Coal Measures have been worked and some locally exceed 1 m in thickness.

The full thickness of the Middle Coal Measures is not present in the County. Only 150 to 170m remain, the rest having been removed by erosion since Carboniferous times. The succession is generally similar to the Lower Coal Measures and includes numerous coals, most of which are less than 1m thick. The base is marked by the Queenslie Marine Band which is a persistent bed of mudstone containing characteristic marine fossils. Ironstones mainly in the Middle Coal Measures were mined at the Devon Colliery alongside the Ironworks.

Intrusive Igneous rocks of Carboniferous and Permian ages

These intrusions are composed of dolerite, and occur mainly as sills but there are a few dykes. Dolerites are hard, generally medium-grained crystalline rocks. Two types are found in the County:- olivine-dolerite, which formed at various times during the Carboniferous; more commonly quartz-dolerite, which was intruded in the early Permian (c.295 m yrs). The quartz-dolerite forms the Midland Valley Sill that crops out prominently around Stirling and forms fault intrusions associated with the Ochil Fault at Alva, Tillicoultry and Dollar. It is quarried at Castle Craigs (NS 913 977).

GEOLOGICAL STRUCTURE

The general structure in the County is only indirectly illustrated by Figure 4 but a north/south horizontal section is presented in Figure 6. The oldest Devonian rocks crop out in the north. Here, the Ochil Anticline trends ENE and the northerly dipping limb is located to the north of the Ochil Fault. The southerly dipping limb of this fold is truncated by this Fault. The axis of the Clackmannan Syncline, a broad downfold, roughly coincides with a north-south line through Alloa with the younger rocks to be found in the central parts of the County. The axis of the syncline corresponds imprecisely with the original centre of subsidence of the Upper Carboniferous sedimentary basin (ie the formations thin to the west and east from the basin centre). There are other smaller folds such as the anticline at Dollarfield (NS 960 970) and the synclines east of Alva (NS 890 970), Tillicoultry (NS 935 980) and Dollar (NS 970 986). The last three trend E-ENE and may be rollover folds related to the development of the Ochil Fault. The structure is dominated by the Ochil Fault. It has a maximum vertical downthrow to the south of about 3000m at Alva and Harviestoun. Here it brings the Lower Devonian volcanic rocks to the north against the Carboniferous Middle Coal Measures to the south. Other faulting is common, with vertical displacements ranging from metre scale (eg in the Windy Edge Pass in Dollar Glen) to more than 750ft/240m. The major faults are aligned roughly east-west or northwest-southeast. Displacement on the faults took place relatively soon after the strata were deposited and, although many fractures were probably reactivated subsequently, there is only one record of undoubted movement in historical times (the 1736 Dollar Earthquake).

The overall pattern of folding and faulting reflects the extensional origin of the geological structure of the Midland Valley of Scotland, but minor sideways slip in a dextral, right lateral, direction took place on some faults.

Earth movements (see also p.16) still occur in Clackmannanshire (Bain 1980 and Burton and Neilson 1979) but their epicentres mainly lie north of the Ochil Fault. Menstrie is closely associated with these modern tremors and features in over half the articles about them eg –

Alloa Advertiser, May 23rd, 1905
"The Menstrie Earthquake
The earthquake is stated to have been no slight tremor, but such a convulsion as to cause articles lying on tables or hanging on walls of houses to rattle considerably while people lying in bed seemed to feel that something was interfering with that part of the earth's surface on which Menstrie stands. The earthquake ... was of short duration with no rumbling noise or tremendous explosion. Such interferences are apt to militate against Menstrie as a health resort and summer retreat, for health and pleasure seekers are like ordinary people and care not to be tossed about on the earth's surface and probably meet the fate of Korah and his company who conspired against the priests of God".

The other inhabitants of the County were not to be outdone, as is shown in the following article:

Alloa Journal and Clackmannanshire Advertiser, September 23, 1905
"A Shocking Occurrence
It looks as though the midget county was about to make a name for itself as

a centre for seismic disturbances ... the district was visited by a pretty severe shock of earthquake, the second in two months. Time was when such occurrences, as far as this district were concerned were confined to ... Menstrie, and the inhabitants of that place had ... the monopoly of earthquake lore. Now things are different and the natives of Alva, Tillicoultry and Dollar and even the aristocratic dwellers in suburban Alloa are becoming quite expert in detailing the 'symptoms'. Apparently the fashionable thing to do immediately after the manifestations have passed away is to rush out of doors in neglige costume to ascertain the extent of the damage and compare notes with one's neighbours."

The mineralisation found in faults and joints in the rocks of the southern Ochils is thought to be of early Permian age. It is associated with the major earth movements that terminated the deposition of Carboniferous sedimentary and volcanic rocks and imposed on them the previously described structural features. The metalliferous ores are most commonly of copper, as at Balquharn, Tillicoultry and Burn of Sorrow above Dollar, with the latter pair also yielding lead ores. Silver was found at Carnaughton Glen, west of Alva and spectacularly at the Alva Silver Glen mines c.1714. Here cobalt was later also extracted, for use in pottery glazes. The 1970s description of the mines and minerals of the Ochils has recently been updated to take account of Dr Moreton's research as to the true silver mine in the Silver Glen (Dickie et al 1994, H in figure 5) and a *Scots Magazine* article is *in press* – due May 1997. The most worked non-metalliferous mineral is barytes, often red in colour due to the presence of haematite. Myreton Hill above Menstrie was once a minor source of calcite for local iron foundries during the Napoleonic Wars when other European sources were unavailable. Neither the mines for barytes nor calcite operated for long, perhaps because of impurities such as haematite, but also because of difficulty of access. The Myreton site (NS 85069807) is unique in having the only track of industrial origin up the steep scarp face of the Ochils – refreshed some years ago by bulldozing to allow access to farm vehicles, it is now more conspicuous.

Post-Permian geological history

From the Permian onwards, Scotland remained as a positive landmass, with sedimentation confined to the fringes. The landmass continued to drift northwards through regions corresponding to the present day Sahara and into the temperate belt. Evidence of the changing environment caused by this northward drift is contained in rocks formed in the post-Permian period. Unfortunately Triassic, Jurassic and Cretaceous age sedimentary rocks are unknown anywhere in central Scotland. There is no evidence therefore of the major sedimentary and tectonic events which led to the development of the hydrocarbon-rich North Sea rocks during this time. However, a veneer of Cretaceous marine sedimentary rocks (chalk) may have been deposited.

The igneous activity associated with the break-up of the continental mass and the opening of the Atlantic in Tertiary times is not represented in the

County. However, the basic topographic configuration of the Devon and Forth valleys may have been fashioned by prolonged erosion during this period. The ultimate consequences of the northward shift in latitude are the ice ages that occurred in the last two million years during the Quaternary Era.

QUATERNARY GEOLOGY – Table 1 and Figure 7

The Quaternary Era was a time of extensive glaciations. However, there is little reliable evidence of the older glacial (and interglacial) events that have affected central Scotland. Indeed, most of the accessible Quaternary deposits and features in the County are less than 30,000 years old (late-Devensian and Flandrian age). Geological history during Quaternary glacial periods is described in time 'slices' called stades and interstades. These represent colder and warmer climatic episodes within a glaciation. A simplified map showing the surface distribution of Quaternary deposits forms Figure 7 and the lithostratigraphical divisions are listed in Table 1.

Pre Dimlington Stade (>27,000 years ago)

There may be pockets of sand and gravel and beds of glacial till that pre-date the Main late-Devensian glaciation of 27,000 years ago. If so, these deposits would be found in so-called 'buried channels'. These elongate, deep hollows in the bedrock surface are probably not ancient river valleys graded to sea-levels (much) lower than present. Rather, their form is probably that of closed basins, the shape suggesting that they are likely to be glacially related scours. A major bedrock depression exists under the Devon valley (100m below OD.) from west of Menstrie to east of Tillicoultry. Interestingly, there is no evidence of similar glacial overdeepening along the line of the Forth valley between Stirling and Kincardine Bridge even though there is to the west of Stirling and also under Grangemouth to offshore of Bo'ness.

Dimlington Stade (c.27,000-13,500 years ago)

The Main late-Devensian ice sheet of the Dimlington Stade eroded the landscape producing striated bedrock surfaces, roche moutonnes and crag and tail features. Both the promontory on which Stirling Castle is sited and Abbey Craig are examples of the last landform. Erosion by the ice removed pre-existing glacial and interglacial sediments and may also have contributed to major changes in the pattern of the pre-glacial (Tertiary) river-system in central Scotland. The ice deposited substantial spreads of glacial till (Wilderness Till Formation) at its base, which it commonly sculpted into streamlined ovoid mounds called drumlins that are typical of lowland ice deposition and erosion. These 'whaleback' ridges taper downstream, thereby indicating the direction of iceflow which in the County is to the east. Clackmannan Tower is located on one such feature (Figure 3), as is Gartmorn Farm steading seen to the north of the newly signposted viewpoint (NS 920 931) at Gartmorn Dam Country Park where typical drumlin scenery abounds. Other drumlins include Lornshill in Alloa.

The till (ground moraine) is generally 4 to 18m thick. Typically the till is dark grey, with a sandy, silty clay matrix containing 'floating' pebbles, cobbles and boulders. Not surprisingly, the local till contains much lava debris in the Ochils where it is found to heights of over 600m OD. on the valley sides.

In the Forth valley area at the acme of glaciation, the 1 km-thick Main late-Devensian ice sheet probably extended 30 or 40km beyond the coast of east Fife. After this ice sheet began to retreat about 16,000 yrs ago, substantial volumes of glaciofluvial sand and gravel (Broomhouse Formation) were deposited by the meltwaters. These ice contact deposits often have characteristic landforms such as mounds, eskers (ridges) and kettle-holes. Such deposits and features are present in the Devon valley east of Tillicoultry and include the Cunninghar ridge (NS 925 973). Meltwater transport was generally eastwards in the Devon valley towards Loch Leven in Kinross-shire, but also north-eastwards at an early stage through the valleys of the Ochil Hills to Glen Devon and to Glen Eagles.

When a thick ice-sheet forms, it imposes a heavy load on the earth's surface. The crust responds by warping downwards, the amount of downwarp being greatest at the centre of accumulation and diminishing to zero a short distance beyond the edge of the ice-sheet. Unloading by melting of the ice is accompanied by crustal uplift (isostatic recovery) in the area of previous depression. The return of water to the oceans from melting land-based ice reverses the effect of world sea-level lowering that occurs during an ice age when water is extracted from the sea to form the ice. The interplay of the local isostatic recovery with world sea-level changes has caused fluctuations in relative sea-level in the Forth area. These are marked by raised beach features and by raised marine deposits.

During deglaciation, local relative sea-level was high in central Scotland and it is not uncommon to find raised marine sediments at about 40 to 45 m above OD. in the Forth and Devon valleys. In this area, the decaying glaciers retreated westwards towards the Highlands. In detail, the retreat of the glacier appears to have halted briefly at Stirling (c.13,500 years ago) where the valley is constricted at the Castle Rock. In the Devon valley, the Cunninghar ridge sand and gravel may have been deposited as the last act of the westward retreating glacier hereabouts. By about 13,000 years ago, the sea had invaded the upper Forth reaching Aberfoyle and occupied the Devon as far east as Dollar. The marine sediments associated with the deglaciation of the Forth valley are finely laminated clay and silt (Loanhead and Kinneil Kerse formations) which contain macro- and micro-fossils which indicate that the local climate was arctic.

The most conspicuous (to geomorphologists only!) of the former coastlines associated with deglaciation in the Forth is the Main Perth Shoreline, tenuously dated to around 13,500 years ago. It has not been recognised west of Alloa (see Figure 8A). The raised beach intertidal platforms may be recognised either by the landform or the presence of sand and gravel (Killearn Formation).

Windermere Interstade (13,500-11,000 years ago

Late-Devensian seabed sediments characteristic of the fully deglaciated sea lochs of the Forth and Loch Lomond area are usually rather massive-looking silty clays (Linwood Formation) which commonly contain many marine fossils. The fauna indicate that the climate was warmer than that before 13,500 yrs ago. Drop-stones in the sediments were probably derived from the melting of rafts of winter shore-ice rather than calved icebergs. The Abbotsgrange Formation in the Grangemouth area, by exception, consists of well-layered pro-delta sediments. Raised beaches, composed of sand and gravel, at Tullibody, Alloa and Kilbagie provide evidence that during the Windermere Interstade local relative sea-level fell from c.40m above OD to present, or below, before glaciers reappeared in central Scotland during the Loch Lomond Stade. During the Interstade the local landscape was largely devoid of trees except for stands of birch, and generally tundra-like with dwarf birch and shrubs, such as crowberry and juniper, sedges and grasses.

Loch Lomond Stade (11,000-10,000 years ago)

The Loch Lomond Stade ice accumulated on Rannoch Moor and in the high corries of the southwest Highlands and advanced into lowland areas to reach Callander and Lake of Menteith in the Teith and Forth valleys respectively. Beyond the ice margins such as in Clackmannanshire, the interstadial soils were destroyed and eroded as much of the local vegetation was killed by the cold leaving open tundra dominated by patches of grasses, sedges and dwarf shrubs. Frozen ground (permafrost) developed and frost wedge casts formed. Materials were also moved downslope by freeze-thaw action. Such solifluction deposits have not yet been identified on geological maps of the County, but they are likely to exist in the Ochils and mantling hillslopes in places on the Clackmannan 'Ridge'.

During the Loch Lomond Stade local relative sea-level in the Forth valley is known to have fallen below that of the present day (Figure 8B). In the Grangemouth area, where the Main Lateglacial Shoreline is widely developed at about OD, it is generally agreed that the level of the sea may have fallen to around 10m below OD. The associated shore platform is normally covered by the 'buried gravel layer' (Bothkennar Gravel Formation) which is usually only about a metre thick. Formation of the platform and the cliffline has been ascribed to enhanced marine erosion under the prevailing periglacial conditions, but shoreline inheritance may also have played a part.

Flandrian Interstade (<10,000 years ago)

About 10,000 years ago, there was a major change in the climate that may have taken place in as little as a hundred years. This was associated with the disappearance of glacial ice from Scotland. From arctic conditions, the climate improved such that birch woodland was widespread within 1000 years. At the postglacial optimum about 6500 years ago, the local climate was warmer and wetter than at the present day and the local landscape dominated by mixed forests of birch, oak, hazel and elm.

From the low during the Loch Lomond Stade, local sea-level rose early in the Flandrian due to the return of water to the oceans from melting land-based ice around the world. The 'High', 'Main' and 'Low Buried Beaches' (at about 8, 7m and over 6m above OD near Menstrie) in the Forth valley formed on the following fall of relative sea-level due to continuing isostatic recovery after the retreat and decay of the Forth Glacier (see Figure 8C). On the exposed surfaces of the deposits of clay, silt and sand, peat was able to accumulate and thus form the well known Sub-Carse Peat which is 0.2-1m thick in this area (Figure 8D). The basal peat on the 'Main Buried Beach' dates from about 9600 yrs ago and on the 'Low Buried Beach' from about 8800 yrs. The deposits of the buried beaches have been assigned to the Letham Formation which contains an impoverished estuarine fauna.

When the main Flandrian marine transgression started about 8000 yrs ago, most of the Sub-Carse Peat was drowned. Extensive fine-grained estuarine sediments of the carse clay were laid down (Claret Formation) in the estuary burying the peat and the underlying High, Main and Low Buried beaches (Figure 8D). The carse clay contains a diverse boreal fauna including the remains of large whales which have been found as far west in the Forth as Cardross near Menteith about 28km to the west of Alloa. Of course, whales have been known to reach Alloa in more recent times and on one occasion a local business man bought the carcase and toured the area charging to view it. Its skeleton is believed to be in the Natural History Museum in London.

In the period between 8000 years ago and the acme of the Flandrian transgression, around 6500 years ago, the whole of the Forth valley-floor west of Stirling silted up as did the Devon valley. At the acme, local relative sea-level reached a maximum of about 16 m above OD in the Aberfoyle area and 13 m above OD in the Devon valley because of the slope on the fossilised estuarine surface caused by the isostatic tilting of the land. This tilting was in response to the continuing relief of the much more significant Main late-Devensian ice loading rather than that of the Loch Lomond Stade.

The Main Flandrian Shoreline, with which these levels are associated, has been widely recognised in the Forth valley from east of Grangemouth to Aberfoyle. It is recognisable north of Cambus and west of Tullibody, in northern Alloa, south of Clackmannan Tower and in the Devon valley. When this shoreline formed about 6500 years ago, the sites of the Hillfoots burghs, Falkirk, Stirling and Aberfoyle were coastal. A Lower Postglacial Shoreline and extensive abandoned intertidal mudflats occur to the south of Alloa and Clackmannan. The Grangemouth Formation, which consists of clay, silt and sand, includes present-day and reclaimed intertidal and subtidal sediments.

As central Scotland is an area of significant overall postglacial fall in sea-level, the consequent incision of the drainage has produced scenically attractive river gorges such as the River Devon at Rumbling Bridge and the Cauldron Linn Waterfall, and the spectacular, partly fault-controlled gorge of Dollar Glen. Features of river erosion in these gorges include potholes and caves. During deglaciation, the waters of the upper part of the Devon catchment flowed eastwards to Loch Leven. The Rumbling Bridge Gorge, initiated as a late stage feature in deglaciation, probably represents a fine example of river capture, causing the headwaters to flow westwards to join the Forth. The River Devon in its lower reaches is meandering, locally with cut-off channels on the floodplain. Our influence on this river, floodbanks apart, include localised examples of uncontrolled waste disposal.

RESOURCES AND OTHER ENVIRONMENTAL ISSUES

Sand and gravel deposits are a valuable source of aggregate and have been extracted locally. Glaciofluvial deposits are the most common but the extensive alluvial cone deposits of the Devon valley may contain large quantities of sand and gravel and boulders. Bings of colliery waste have potential for use as bulk fill, for provision of mudstone for brick-making or for the recovery of their coal content. Tips in the region have been landscaped and much of the material redistributed and used in land reclamation and in industrial redevelopment. Locally the fine-grained deposits of the Claret (carse clay) and Loanhead formations could be exploited for brick and tile manufacture as the latter has been at Hilton near Alloa.

In the past the main natural resource within Clackmannanshire was deep-mined coal but prolonged extraction from over 250 shafts and adits sunk since about 1650 has depleted the reserves to such an extent that large-scale underground mining is now limited to extraction of the Upper Hirst Seam at the Longannet Complex. Polluting waters from abandoned mines have been, and are, an ongoing environment problem (Forth River Purification Board 1995-6). Opencast coal has already been obtained from the Lower Coal Measures. Opencast coal extraction can be an economic way of preparing unstable land underlain by shallow mineworkings for future development, but also environmentally disastrous for people and wildlife.

Hydrocarbons have been prospected for with little success at Inch of Ferryton (NS 90 90), south of Clackmannan by Tricentrol Oil. A local newspaper headline at the time declared 'Oil rigs in the Ochils?' wrongly suggesting an interest in Lower Devonian volcanic rocks. Commercial activity is centred currently on coal-bed methane.

There are resources of hardrock aggregate in the County from the outcrops of quartz-dolerite and especially in the thermally metamorphosed volcanic rocks which are currently exploited at Castle Craigs Quarry (NS 913 977), Tillicoultry. Sandstone is found throughout the local sedimentary sequence and some beds were formerly quarried for building stone. Sandstones of the Passage Formation have potential as a source of silica sand. Alloa is where much of the local crushed sandstone is processed into glass. There are resources of fireclay in the Passage Formation and to a lesser extent in the lower part of the Lower Coal Measures which could be worked opencast.

Metalliferous ores, including lead and barytes, are present in Lower

Devonian rocks. Silver and cobalt were once mined in the Ochil Hills as noted above at p.10.

Groundwater has not been a key resource in the area for water supply, but it is likely that its development, particularly in the Passage Formation, will take place as the cost of water increases. Alloa is noteworthy for its two breweries. The Thistle Brewery of Maclay and Co Ltd. is the only one in Scotland still with its own water supply. The brewing industry in Alloa was established in the late 19th century because of available 'Burton' type groundwaters in the underlying Carboniferous rocks. The sandstones of the Lower Coal Measures and Passage Formation are permeable to some extent, with faults and interbedded mudstones making the aquifer rather complex. Abundant recharge is available allegedly from the streams of the Ochil Hills. The Brewery has two 183m deep supply boreholes drilled in 1924 and 1952. During 1983, the older well dried up and a television inspection by the British Geological Survey revealed that the walls had become encrusted with iron hydroxide deposits. The cause of this precipitation was the mixing of shallow oxygenated water with deeper highly reducing waters which carried iron in solution. The well was reamed out to a bigger diameter and output then returned to normal.

Geothermal power may be available from deeply buried aquifers such as the aeolian sandstones of the Upper Devonian Knox Pulpit Formation (Table 1).

The importance of running waters to the area during the industrial revolution was reflected in the number of woollen mills, the wood dam in Tillicoultry Glen and lades to power drainage operations in the mines etc. The fast flowing streams emerging from the glens at the foot of the Ochil scarp have built alluvial cones where the marked change in slope causes rapid deposition of the transported sediments as the water velocity is suddenly checked. Historically these areas were perceived as dry sites relative to the then poorly drained valley floor and so the earliest Hillfoots settlements were located on them. However the Tillicoultry flood of August 1877, after a deluge of rain, was associated with a wall of water about 2m in height coming down the Burn with tragic and considerable financial consequences. In this town and also Alva, recent building has taken place on land once regarded as problematical because of drainage difficulties.

Although most geohazards affecting Scotland (as at p.9 above) are not likely to be on the scale represented by volcanic eruptions or large earthquakes with major loss of life, the financial burden caused by landslip, collapse of mineworkings etc. could be significant locally. Examples include

Alloa Journal, August 13, 1927
There is a good deal of divergence of local opinion as to the cause. This may be ... due to the giving way of the underground workings of a long-disused colliery known as Harper's Neuk. It was understood that this colliery had been worked on what is known as the 'stoop and room' principle, pillars of coal being left in as supports. However the Harper's Neuk colliery which

was closed over 130 years ago was only in operation a short time. The theory is therefore gaining ground that the subsidences were due to a kind of earthquake possibly occasioned by some geological 'fault' in the strata beneath the area where the sinkings took place."

Alloa Advertiser, June 28, 1952
"River Devon Disappears
'No danger' says Coal Board Official.
The Black Devon has disappeared – for its last two miles it is only a black mud channel, punctuated with old tyres and barrels, along which the tide swirls and falls back. The river water is going down a hole, possibly forty feet across, which, the guess is - leads to old Shore pit workings. On Wednesday it was discovered ... the water was running over a small waterfall and disappearing down into this hole. Not only river water was going down the hole. With every tide the salt water from the Forth came flowing up and poured down the hole, which is half a mile below the tidal limit. The Coal Board believe that new mining under very old workings has caused the supports in the old works to collapse, bringing down the roof and the bed of the river."

Alloa and Hillfoots Advertiser, May 1, 1992
"Probe into mystery of earth tremors
Castlebridge Mine is to commission a major study to try to discover the cause of mysterious earth tremors which are shaking the Forestmill area. Frightened residents heard that pit officials are as baffled by the tremors as they are."

Landslips have happened in the Hillfoots in the areas of the brown forest soils and skeletal soils that cling to the steep face of the Ochils (Figure 1). One recent notable example occurred in the early hours of Sunday 4th November 1984, when a slope failure on Myreton Hill allowed c.350m^3 of debris to slip downhill. A combination of soil cover type - Brown Forest Soil over glacial till with a sandy matrix, the intense storm on the 3rd/4th November (which followed a long period of above-normal precipitation) and the slope of the hillside (between 30° and 40°) contributed to the slip which resulted in Broomhall Cottage being inundated by the flow of debris. Up to 1m depth of material entered the house through doors and windows. Evidence of the force of the flow of material was provided by the formation on the transport slope of a natural trench up to 2m deep which was not evident before the event. The back feature of the 'Main Postglacial Shoreline' at the Pleasure Grounds in Alloa has also been affected by landslip. Coastal erosion and flooding may be enhanced by rising sea-level associated with the greenhouse effect thus threatening areas of reclaimed land east of Alloa and also the Inches.

REFERENCES AND FURTHER READING

Bain, Iain. 1980. Why the Borders Shook on Boxing Day. *Forth Naturalist and Historian* 5, 3-6.

Baird, W. J. 1989. The Scenery of Scotland – the Structure Beneath. *Forth Naturalist and Historian* 11, 3-18.

Browne, M. A. E. 1987. The physical geography and geology of the estuary and Firth of Forth, Scotland. *Proceedings of the Royal Society of Edinburgh* 93B, 235-44.

Browne, M. A. E., *et al*. 1984. Quaternary estuarine deposits in the Grangemouth area, Scotland. Report of the British Geological Survey 16, No.3.

Browne, M. A.E., *et al*. 1987. The Upper Devonian and Carboniferous sandstones of the Midland Valley of Scotland. Investigation of the geothermal potential of the UK. British Geological Survey Open-File Report.

Browne, M. A. E., and Mendum, J. 1995. Loch Lomond to Stirling. A landscape fashioned by geology. Scottish Natural Heritage and British Geological Survey.

Burton, P. W. and Neilson, N. E. 1979. Earthquake sworms: in Scotland. *Forth Naturalist and Historian* 4, 3-36.

Cameron, I. B. and Stephenson, D. 1985. The Midland Valley of Scotland. British Regional Geology. Third edition. HMSO: London.

Corbett, L. *et al*. 1993. Central Scotland – land, wildlife, people. Forth Naturalist and Historian, Stirling University.

Corbett, L., Roy, E. K., and Snaddon, R. C. 1994. The Ochil Hills – landscape, wildlife, heritage, walks. Forth Naturalist and Historian and Clackmannanshire Field Studies Society.

Craig, G. Y., Editor. 1991. Geology of Scotland. Third Edition. The Geological Society.

Dickie, D. M. *et al*. 1994. Mines and Minerals of the Ochils. Clackmannanshire Field Studies Society. Temporary reprint with corrigenda of the original 1974 edition.

Dinham, C. H. and Haldane, D., 1932. The Economic Geology of the Stirling and Clackmannan Coalfield. Memoir of the Geological Survey of Great Britain.

Findlay, I. 1986. Mill Glen Trail Guide, Tillicoultry. Clackmannan District Council.

Forth River Purification Board – papers and displays, 1995-6.

Francis, E. H., *et al*. M., 1970. The geology of the Stirling district. Memoir of the Geological Survey of Great Britain.

Gostelow, T. P. and Browne, M. A. E. 1981. Engineering geology of the Upper Forth Estuary. Open-File Report of the Institute of Geological Sciences.

Monro, S. K., Cameron, I. B. and Hall, I. H. S. 1991. Geology for land use planning: Stirling. British Geological Survey, Technical Report WA/91/25.

National Trust for Scotland. 1991. Dollar Glen Guide.

Price, R. J. 1983. Scotland's environment during the last 30,000 years. Scottish Academic Press: Edinburgh.

Rippon, J., Read, W. A. and Park, R. G. 1996. The Ochil Faults and the Kincardine basin: key structures in the tectonic evolution of the Midland Valley of Scotland. *The Journal of the Geological Society* 153, 573-587.

Sissons, J. B. 1974. Quaternary in Scotland: a review. *Scottish Journal of Geology*, 10, 34-87.

Sissons, J. B., 1976. Geomorphology of the British Isles: Scotland. Methuen.

Sutherland, D. G. 1984. The Quaternary deposits and landforms of Scotland and the neighbouring shelves: a review. *Quaternary Science Reviews* 3, 157-254

Taylor, A, and Nortcliff, S. 1996. Soils. Scotland's Living Landscapes. Scottish Natural Heritage. 22pp.

Walker, P. M. B., Editor. 1991. Chambers Earth Sciences Dictionary.

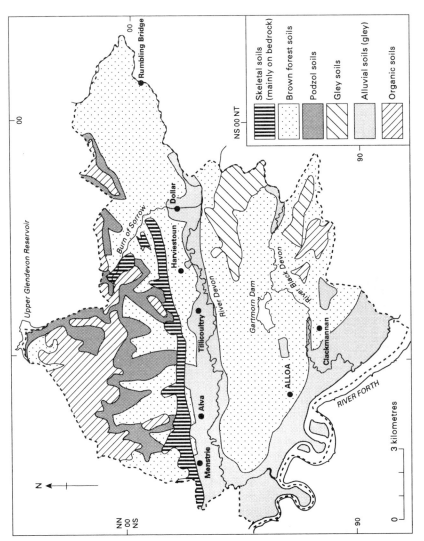

Figure 1. Clackmannanshire soils.

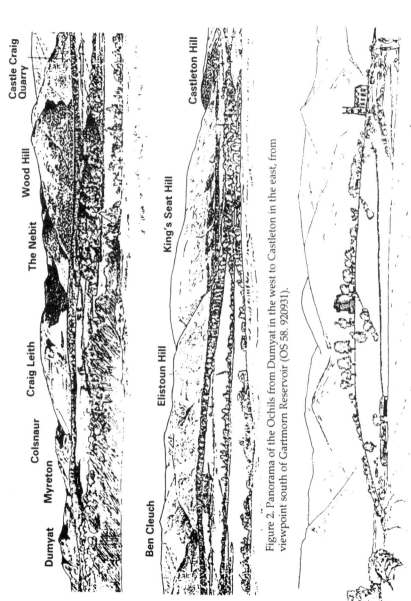

Figure 2. Panorama of the Ochils from Dumyat in the west to Castleton in the east, from viewpoint south of Gartmorn Reservoir (OS 58. 920931).

Figure 3. Clackmannan 'Ridge' – glacially streamlined drumlin hill underlying Clackmannan Tower, viewed from the south – ice movement was west to east.

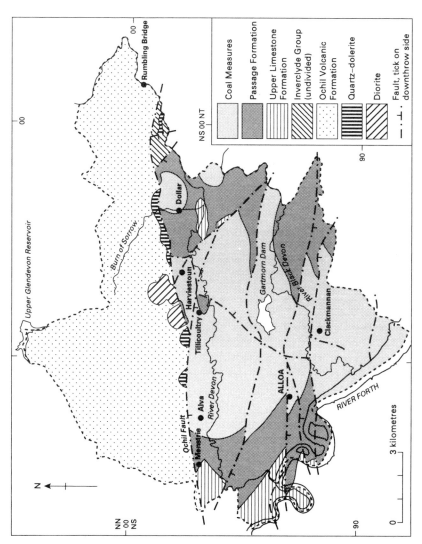

Figure 4. Bedrock geology map of Clackmannanshire.

Environment		Lithology	Flora/fauna
Tropical (or Warm Temperate) Forest		Coal/peat	Plants
Soil (palaeosol)		Fireclay/seatearth	Roots
Delta Topsets including river channels		Sandstone with large scale cross-bedding	
Delta Foresets		Sandstone with ripple (small scale) cross bedding	Drifted plant remains
Delta front		Siltstone and sandstone interbedded with flat and ripple lamination	Burrows and rare marine or freshwater mussels
Delta Bottomsets			
Pro-delta offshore, muddy water		Mudstone flat bedded with ironstone/limestone nodules	Marine eg brachiopods goniatites mussels
Offshore, clear water		Limestone	Brachiopods corals sea-lilies (crinoids)
Offshore, muddy water		Mudstone	*Lingula* and mussels
Estuary/lake		Siltsone and sandstone	Freshwater or estuarine mussels, burrows
Tropical Forest		Coal	Plants
Soil		Fireclay/seatearth	Roots

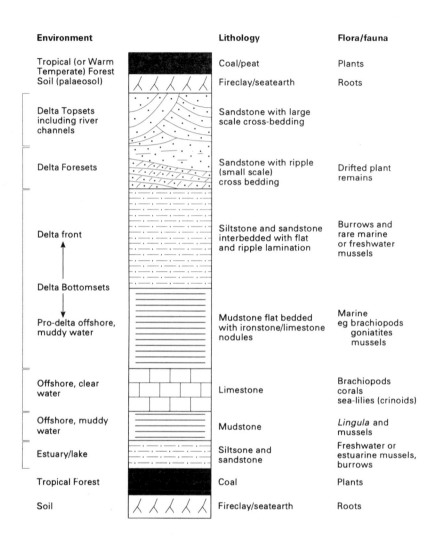

Figure 5. Typical Carboniferous sedimentary cycle.

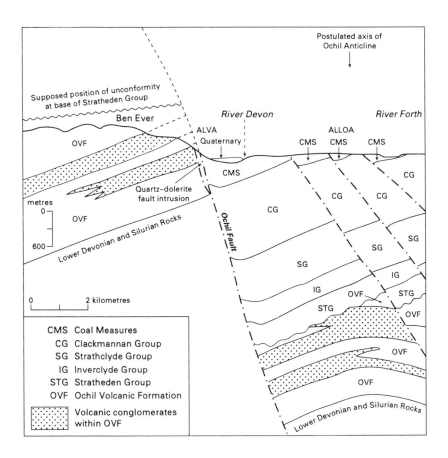

Figure 6. North-south geological cross-section from Ben Ever to the River Forth.

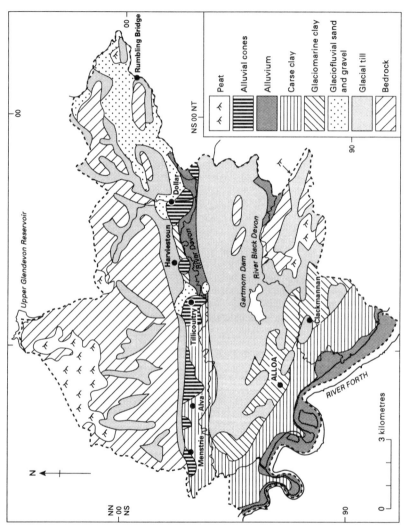

Figure 7. Quaternary geology of Clackmannanshire.

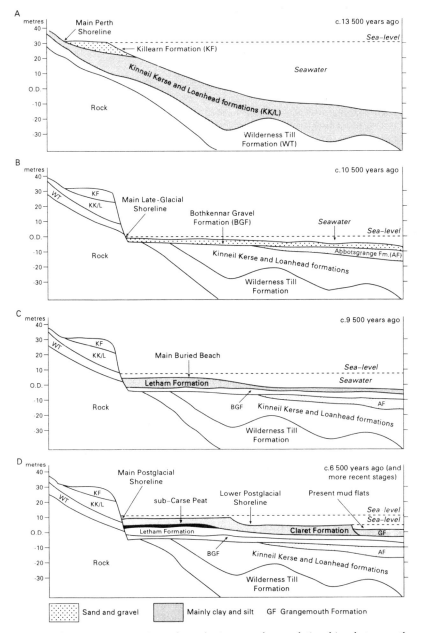

Figure 8. Diagrammatic sections through time to show relationships between the Quaternary sediments, former beaches and sea-levels, in the Alloa area of the Forth.

Reviews (Naturalist)

Loch Lomond: showing the West Highland Way, Ardlui to Milngavie. Ordnance Survey, Outdoor Leisure map 39, 1:25,000 (2½"/mile). ISBN 0-319-26065-8. £5.40.

Double sided, full colour, it traces the route of the Way right from Milngavie to Inverarnan and Glen Falloch, and the whole length of Loch Lomond. Its great detail includes mountain rescue facilities and visitor information – car parks, boat hire, and cruising bases, camp sites, information centres, picnic areas, viewpoints, public toilets, youth hostels.... Spread out for study it takes up a full 4' x 3' of floor. The southern area side, landscape format, stretches from Milgavie to Balmaha, includes the south end of Loch Lomond, the Clyde river from Dalmuir/Erskine Bridge through Dumbarton to the Firth beyond Greenock into the south end of Loch Long. The other side, picturewise oriented, details the Way Balmaha to Inverarnan and Glen Falloch; eastwards from Inversnaid through Loch Arklet and Loch Chon with Stronachlachar and part of Loch Katrine; westwards are upper Loch Long, Arrochar, the Alps, Loch Sloy.

Truly here is a real mine of information, and pleasure.

LC

Discovering the River Forth. William F. Hendrie. John Donald. ISBN 0.85976.438.9. £2.50.

This interesting and informative book takes the reader through 18 chapters for a walk down the shores of the Forth from Aberfoyle to Queensferry. The narrative, which is easy to read and in a lively style, is interspersed with reminiscences of the author, and a wide variety of historical anecdotes ranging from a secret nuclear bunker at Aberfoyle, to the early Carron engineer presented with the seeds of a new root vegetable by the King of Sweden – now known as 'swedes'! The material covered is exclusively 'social' history, and no attempt is made to include any 'natural' history.

The title is also somewhat misleading in that, according to many sources (e.g. Royal Society, Edinburgh, 1987), the 'Forth' from Aberfoyle to Stirling is 'River', Stirling to Queensferry being tidal, and progressively saltier, is regarded as 'Estuary'; and beyond Queensferry is 'Firth'.

Whilst the book has an index, it has no references on sources of further reading – which might have included some natural history! Even substantial quotations are inadequately referenced. This is a considerable shame as readers have no help to delve further into any topic that may take their fancy. Despite these reservations it is a treasury of information on the towns and villages of the 'Forth Valley', and we can only hope that author and publisher might remedy these matters in any future editions.

D. McLusky

THE CORBETTS OF CENTRAL SCOTLAND
A Hillwalker's Introduction

Ian Collie

The British expedition which went out to survey the Himalayas last century identified the highest mountain in the world and originally labelled it 'No. 15', which seemed hardly appropriate so they named it after their leader, George Everest (later Sir George Everest). Thus he became immortalised among mountaineers, a happy fate shared by a select few including John R. Corbett who earlier this century listed all Scottish hills of height 2500ft-3000ft, each with a separation drop of at least 500ft from any similar neighbour. Corbett was a district valuer based in Bristol, a keen climber who completed the Munros in 1930; he climbed also all Scottish hills over 2000ft. It's doubtful whether he would have foreseen that guides to the hills classified in his name would be produced; e.g. the Scottish Mountaineering Trust's current edition lists 221 Corbetts, the total having changed now and then over the years as a result of fresh measurements.

The total of Corbetts in Central Scotland, like the national total, could be open to some measure of debate. It would appear that there are 10 within the boundary, and five actually on the boundary itself. The list is as follows.

Ten within Central Scotland:
Beinn a' Choin; Stob a' Choin; Stob Fear-tomais; Ben Ledi; Benvane; Meall an t-Seallaidh; Creag MacRanaich; Beinn Each; Ben nan Imirean; Beinn Chaorach (just!)

Five on the boundary:
Creag Uchdag (Boundary with former Tayside)
Beinn Chuirn (Boundary with former Strathclyde)
Beinn Odhar (Boundary with former Strathclyde)
Cam Chreag (Boundary with former Tayside and Strathclyde)
Beinn nan Oighreag (Boundary with former Tayside)

There is one other, Meall nan Subh, whose summit seems to lie just outwith the boundary in former Tayside near Ben Lawers. In such a case it would be interesting to know the reasoning of the surveyors. All the judgements listed have been taken on the basis of Ordnance Survey 1:50,000 maps, and - as indicated - there could be room for argument! The sketch map gives approximate locations.

The following brief notes on each hill are offered from the point of view of a humble hill-walker and not from the viewpoint of a specialist in geology, ornithology or any other 'ology'.

Ben Ledi 2883ft/879m. (Mountain of the gentle slope.) GR 563098. OS 57.

The list already given was ordered according to the Corbetts guide, but Ben

Ledi is now placed first because it is by far the best known of the Central Scotland Corbetts and arguably the most familiar one in Scotland since its commanding situation makes it visible virtually from Edinburgh to Glasgow.

The tourist sentinel on the battlements of Stirling Castle immediately focuses on its fine outlines as the first rampart of the Highlands, and probably resolves to see it at closer hand rising impressively above Callander. The first snows on Ben Ledi herald the start of winter to folk in Central Scotland, and throughout the year its seasonal moods are the subject of familiar, perhaps daily, attention. Its popularity as a hill to climb is attested by a parking area beside the Leny which can be well filled on any weekend throughout the year, the tracks thronged with happy folk of all ages and descriptions pleased to make, or remake, first hand acquaintance with this hill which may have dominated their existence. The most common route is along the forest track leading up from the car park but a good circular route can be achieved via Stank Glen.

Corbett's dictum about separation from neighbours means that virtually every hill commands good views all round, and that is certainly the case with Ben Ledi, the aspect towards Loch Lubnaig being particularly attractive. It is hardly surprising that such a prominent summit should feature in local folklore and there are several publications which dwell on this dimension.

Benvane 2694ft/823m. (White mountain.) GR 535137. OS 57.

Unlike its neighbour, Ben Ledi, this is a shy retiring hill whose outlines cannot be well seen from any public viewpoint, but it too offers a rewarding ascent. It can be reached by a fairly strenuous circular walk from Ben Ledi over Stuc Dubh, or by shorter access from Kipp in Strathyre, or from Ballimore Farm at Balquhidder. In winter on the last named route the walker can be guaranteed to see deer foraging on the lower slopes, and to feel keenly the icy threatening blasts on the long ridge to the summit.

Beinn Each 2667ft/817m. (Mountain of the horse.) GR 602158. OS 57.

Maybe Benvane was called 'White Hill' by our Gaelic forebears because it seems to attract and retain snow, but it is not at all apparent why this one should be 'of the horse'. Perhaps some poem or saga in a long-vanished ceilidh would have explained all. As a generalisation, it can be said that hills in southern Scotland are grassy and steep-sided, while Highland hills are heathery and rounded. The western Highlands and Skye have their own characteristics! Beinn Each is very much a southerner and as usual there is a scramble up steep grassy slopes rising from the popular pass of Glen Ample linking Loch Lubnaig and Loch Earn. Grand names - and an attraction for Munro-bagger or Corbett-bagger is to roll them comfortably off the tongue in bothy or banquet. A burn side on the east of the right of way is the best access and eventually leads along an old fence to the summit. The labour involved in past days in making dykes and then fences is always a matter of wonder and speculation.

Stob Fear-tomhais 2531ft/771m. (Surveyor's Peak.) GR 474163. OS 57.

The Gaelic name can be explained in this case as there is a triangulation pillar to mark the top, and the name is a straight translation from English. As surveying is now all done by satellites, these pillars are obsolete and when they have all disappeared there will be folk wondering why this particular title was applied to the hill - that is, if generations long into the future will bother with such matters! The access is initially via the right of way running from Ballimore to Glen Finglas but the walker keeps straight on when the path swings south, and he or she must cross instead the Glean Dubh burn. There is a footbridge further up which should always be used in spate conditions since burns at these times are exceptionally dangerous and have claimed many victims. The way up passes a sheiling beside a large rock, a bit of a puzzle in that it is so unusually close to settlements, but no doubt boys clambered up that rock and pronounced themselves kings of the castle. If only stones could speak! The summit gives grand views of Ben Ledi, Benvane and many of the other Central Scotland Corbetts.

Stob a'Choin 2850ft/865m. (Peak of the dog.) GR 417160. OS 56.

Nearby there is another peak of the dog, and one can only wonder why two hills in reasonable proximity should feature dogs. The outline of the Corbett provides no clue in its prominent rise above the road from Balquhidder to the tourist information point near Inverlochlarig Farm. Beyond the farm there is a footbridge over the river Larig and the route then follows the river upstream before it is necessary to turn south and tackle the craggy steep flank of the hill. The need to negotiate these crags suggests that a day with good visibility should be chosen. As in other areas, land management concerns such as sheep farming must be respected. If the Corbetts already listed have been ascended, the summit gives a satisfying feeling of familiarity with the area. Thoughts of Rob Roy's latter days at Inverlochlarig come to mind and are revived by the number of tourists around Balquhidder kirk.

Meall an t-Seallaidh 2794ft/825m. (Round hill of the sight.) GR 542234. OS 51.

The Gaelic name is again a matter of conjecture. The approach is from the Kirkton Glen pass from Balquhidder, with Loch Eireannaich at the summit, and there is a story that the ghost of a Victorian deer hunter and his dogs can sometimes be seen. But that would be long after the Gaelic name was applied, and so its origins remain a mystery. This is one of the less distinguished of the Central Scotland Corbetts, being just a long, straggly ridge, but its rough terrain can pose quite a challenge, not least in bad weather when navigational skills can be stretched.

Creag MacRanaich 2654ft/809m. (MacRanaich's Crag.) GR 546256. OS 51.

Mount Everest is Sir George Everest's mountain. But who was MacRanaich? An incomer from Rannoch? Possibly some scholar may have the answer, but even the surname itself appears to have disappeared from common view. This hill can be linked by a traverse from Meal an t-Seallaidh or climbed on its own from the Glen Dochart end of the Craigton Pass. Either way its grassy bulwarks require a fair degree of exertion. The summit provides a spacious viewpoint and a good appreciation of the impressive cliffs forming the eastern edge of the two Corbetts in these parts.

Beinn Chaorach 2685ft/818m. (Mountain of the sheep.) GR 359328. OS 50.

This Corbett is just inside the boundary and can be reached directly from the A95 road at Auchtertyre Farm, where an estate road leads up under the railway bridge and on to the hill. The slopes head up at a uniform angle, and the obvious signs of experiment with sheep fencing make the hill's name appropriate. The summit appears to be more enclosed than usual because of the positioning of the neighbouring Corbetts and the general lie of the land, and there is not the usual impression of space and distance.

Beinn nan Imirean 2785ft/849m. (Mountain of the ridge.) GR 419309. OS 51.

This hill is just inside the border, and at first glance it appears to be part of the Munro, Meall Glas, but obviously Corbett had satisfied himself about its status. It can be approached from Glen Lochay but the shorter way is from Glen Dochart where cars can be parked at a lay-by near the entrance to Auchessan Farm. Beyond the farm, a burn points the way to a rather long yomp over bog and hag until the higher ground of the upper reaches is gained. The hill itself does not have much character, but then neither do the others in this somewhat featureless corner of the mountains. Low-flying jets can certainly stir up the scene but their presence is not necessarily welcome. Stalking takes place here as on most of the Corbetts, and estate management has to be respected.

Beinn a'Choin 2525ft/770m. (Mountain of the dog.) GR 354130. OS 56.

Rob Roy would have been familiar with all the Corbetts in Central Scotland, and certainly with this one standing above his home territory of Glen Gyle at the head of Loch Katrine. The access is from Corriearklet farm on the shores of Loch Arklet, and there are east and west ridges which can be combined to form a pleasant circuit. The summit commands a panorama of the Trossachs, including Loch Katrine and all the other romantic country which inspired Sir Walter Scott.

The Boundary Corbetts

Creag Uchdag 2883ft/879m. (Crag of the hollows.) GR 708323. OS 51.

The Central Scotland starting point for this Corbett is on Loch Tay at Ardeonaig, where the Region sadly had to close the school in the 1980s when the roll dropped to two - a far cry from a century previously when the district was populous and there were over 50 in the school. The sheep farmers in these parts forbid dogs but otherwise there should be no problem of access. The way up from Ardeonaig is steep but straightforward and not too long, with good views sweeping down the loch. The summit itself is not distinctive, being set in undulating uplands of grass and heather. There is an alternative access from the dam in Glen Lednock above Comrie.

Beinn nan Oighreag 2982ft/909m. (Cloudberry or hare mountain.) GR 542412. OS 51.

The approach is by a tarred road not far past the power station in Glen Lochay. At the head of the road a path strikes left, following the route of what may have been a miniature railway when the hydro works were in progress. Some way along, a dyke is crossed, and it is the dyke which should be followed as it leads to the Lairig Breisleich, which may have been the principal route between Killin and Glen Lyon in former times. At the foot of the hill proper there is a bonnie sheiling, one of whose houses is very well preserved with the gables standing intact. The ridge walk to the summit is a pleasant affair along a springy, tundra-like surface, and the top gives excellent prospects of all the main peaks around, with familiar features further afield such as Buchaille Etive Mhor, Ben Nevis and the Grey Corries.

Cam Chreag 2900ft/885m. (Crooked crag.) GR 375346. OS 50.

This hill, uniquely in the area, is the meeting place of three former regions as opposed to being fully within Central Scotland or being shared with one other area. The top of Cam Chreag is shared by Central, Strathclyde and Tayside. It shares another distinction along with Beinn Chaorach and Beinn Odhar: it can be included in a strenuous excursion encompassing five Corbetts, a most unusual opportunity since it is not all that easy to link even two such summits together because of the rule about separation. Cam Chreag is not too easy to reach and the going is quite 'yompy' but it is a pleasant enough hill though distinctive qualities tend to be lost in the plethora of this area. Probably the best way to tackle it is to link it with Ben Chaorach.

Beinn Odhar 2955ft/901m. (Dun-coloured mountain.) GR 338339. OS 50.

This boundary Corbett can be combined with a short walk up part of the West Highland Way from Tyndrum,or alternatively a car can be parked at a layby on the Glencoe road beside the railway bridge. Basically the climb is a long unrelenting slog up the slope ahead, but there is an attractive lochan hiding quite near the top – large tadpoles were seen here one mid-October. Some scree and boulders mark the summit and there is a good prospect of the fine sweep of Ben Dorain towards upper Glen Orchy.

Beinn Chuirn 2878/880m. (Mountain of the rocky heap.) GR 281292. OS 50.

This boundary hill above Tyndrum marks a far outpost of Central Scotland, many times removed from the industrial lowlands around the Forth. One access is from Tyndrum via a private forestry track to Glen Cononish with its gold mine workings, and the other is from Glen Lochy where it is necessary to find a railway bridge across the river. The Cononish route passes by the prominent Eas Anie waterfall, and beyond it the slopes become less severe. As on Beinn Odhar, a lochan lies just below the summit, presenting the familiar puzzle of how such lochans are full when there is hardly any ground above from which water can be collected. Ben Lui is one of its more prominent neighbours seen from the summit.

Note of caution

All the Corbetts in Central Scotland can usually be climbed easily enough in summer conditions, but winter can present a different story altogether and unhappily there have been several fatalities. Standard precautions should be always taken.

References

McNeish, Cameron. The Corbett Almanac. 1994. NWP. 160pp.
Ordnance Survey Maps. Landranger 1:50,000 (1¼" to mile) – sheets 50, 51, 56, 57.
Scottish Mountaineering Club. Hillwalker's Guide, volume 2. The Corbetts and Other Scottish Hills. 1996. 250pp.

CENTRAL REGION
CORBETTS – APPROXIMATE LOCATIONS

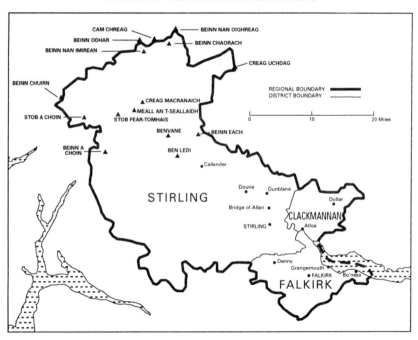

THE WEATHER OF 1995

S. J. Harrison
University of Stirling

The year provided an interesting roller-coaster ride, from baking heat to intense Arctic cold, and from drought to flood. January provided a mixture of snow, gales and floods in Britain. Flooding was exceptionally severe in Western Europe. A warm and dry April promised an early start to summer but then snow fell in mid-May! The three summer months were, on the whole, exceptionally hot, culminating in a scorching August which broke records everywhere. This was accompanied by drought in England and Wales but July provided much needed summer moisture in Scotland. October was amongst the warmest on record in the United Kingdom but December plunged us into the lowest temperatures since the very cold winter of 1981-82, many people facing burst pipes at New Year. The air temperature and rainfall variation during the year is illustrated in Figures 1 and 2.

Temperature and rainfall values in the following refer to Parkhead I although reference has also been made to the records from Bridge of Allan, and Dunblane.

January. Cloudy and damp with occasional snow.

The year started with three cold days in a fresh northerly breeze. Snow lay on the 1st and 2nd, the minimum temperature falling to –7.2°C by the morning of the 3rd (–8.9°C Bridge of Allan). Daytime temperatures struggled to reached 3°C and had only risen to –1.5°C by 13.15 GMT in Bridge of Allan on the 3rd. Between the 4th and 10th rain with occasional sunny spells dominated the weather and the daytime temperature reached an unseasonally mild 11.1°C on the 7th. The wind began to freshen south-westerly on the 15th and the Met Office issued storm warnings. Gales and driving rain affected much of Scotland in the early hours of the 16th but had died away by midday. On the 17th and 18th there was widespread storm damage after which, blustery showers began to fall as snow. The 19th was cold in a brisk easterly and further snow fell later in day. The five-day precipitation total for the 15th to 19th was 44.8mm (54.8mm Bridge of Allan; 56.0mm Dunblane). Further rain fell, often in strong and blustery winds, between the 21st and 24th, much of which fell as snow on ground above 900ft (275m). After 14.30 on the 27th heavy continuous snow was falling in the Stirling area and by the morning of the 28th 5cm had accumulated in Bridge of Allan, which lay until the 30th. Clear skies overnight on the 29th/30th caused temperatures to fall to –7.0°C but they rose quickly on the 30th. Heavy overnight rain fell in a strong south-westerly (28.0mm Parkhead; 25.5mm Bridge of Allan) and the Allan was in flood on the 31st for the first time since mid-December 1994.

February. Wet and windy.

Strong winds and heavy rain fell overnight on the 2nd/3rd and the Allan was in flood again. A fresh WSW wind blew from the 4th to 7th and brought occasional rain with lengthy sunny spells. Rain, which was heavy at times in a blustery wind, fell every day between the 11th and 16th and was accompanied by thunder on the 14th and hail on the 15th. On the 16th the wind veered toward the north-west and the showers turned to sleet. By the evening of the 19th heavy snow was falling, which lay on higher ground above 500ft (153m). The weather became very wet and windy on the 21st and 22nd with protracted spells of sleet and snow in a wind which reached gale-force at times. The 48h precipitation total was 24.8mm (36.8mm Bridge of Allan; 40.2mm Dunblane) and the Allan was in flood. There were four calm days from the 23rd with long sunny spells, but minimum temperatures fell below freezing, reaching –3.2°C at Parkhead on the 24th, and –5.2°C in both Bridge of Allan and Dunblane on the 26th. There was a return to wind and rain on the 27th.

March. Cold and raw with occasional snow.

Snow lying on the 1st set the scene for a cold and raw month during which snow or sleet fell on 12 days and there were 17 air frosts. Cold air continued to be drawn in from the Arctic and intermittent snow fell on the first two days. After a slight thaw on the 3rd, snow returned during the afternoon of the 4th. In a freshening westerly wind, blizzard conditions persisted for a while but the snow-depth on open ground reached only 4cm. Showers of sleet or snow continued until the 8th when there was a change to warmer, but windy and wet, weather. By the morning of the 10th the snowline in the Ochil Hills had retreated to 1500ft (458m). Daytime temperatures rose to 11.2°C by the 13th (12.8°C Bridge of Allan), although the weather was generally rather dull. However, there was heavy snow on the 14th, which lay to a depth of 2cm by the following morning. A fresh to strong north-westerly airstream became established on the 16th, bringing spells of sleet, which were protracted at times. The 16th was particularly wet with 10.6mm in Bridge of Allan and 17.4mm in Dunblane. The wind then freshened south-westerly and the air temperature rose in lengthy sunny spells, reaching 11.2°C on the 23rd (13.0°C Bridge of Allan). Cold Arctic air returned on the 23rd and by the 26th sleet was falling in a freshening northerly which gusted to 38mph at the University. On the 28th there was continuous snow which lay for a short while, after which air temperatures fell in a cold northerly breeze, dropping to –4.0°C on the 29th (–5.0°C Bridge of Allan; –6.7°C Dunblane). A mild south-westerly airstream then raised the daytime temperature which reached 14.2°C on the 31st (15.2°C Bridge of Allan).

April. Warm and very dry.

The weather was unsettled over the first five days but there were three warm and sunny days from the 6th to the 8th, the temperature reaching 14.5°C on the 7th (15.9°C Bridge of Allan). For the following seven days there was an extended spell of warm and dry weather and the daytime maximum temperature topped 20°C in Bridge of Allan on the 12th and 13th (19oC Parkhead on 13th). As Easter approached, a cooler westerly breeze developed which persisted until Easter Monday, when the wind veered north-westerly, drawing in cold air from the Arctic Ocean. Snow began to fall at 00.15 BST on the 18th, bringing the snowline down to 1200ft (366m) in the Ochil Hills, and by 09.00 BST the minimum temperature had fallen to −2.6°C (−3.6°C Bridge of Allan; -3.8°C Dunblane). The cold spell lasted until the 21st, although the north-westerly breeze gradually weakened. By the evening of the 22nd heavy rain was falling in a blustery north-east wind (24h rainfall: 7.0mm Parkhead; 8.9mm Bridge of Allan; 13.0mm Dunblane). From the 24th the weather remained fine away from the east coast but further frosts occurred on the 27th and 29th under clear skies as the breeze dropped away. Although April is not infrequently dry, the month was exceptional in that the total rainfall in the Stirling area was of the order of 20mm, only one-third of the long-term average.

May. Relatively warm.

The 1st was warm and sunny but cloud increased on the 2nd heralding three very dull days, the 4th being sultry, reaching 24.6°C in Bridge of Allan. There was cloud and rain on the 8th after which the temperature fell in a light north-westerly breeze, the maximum temperature reaching only 10.1°C on the 11th. Slight amounts of rain fell as sleet and snow on the 12th but from the 15th the rain was more showery in nature. The last spring frost was recorded in Bridge of Allan on the 19th (air −1.0°C; grass −1.1°C). The 20th and 21st were fine days but rain returned late on the 21st, and also fell overnight on the 24th/25th, which was the wettest 24-hour period of the month (10.4mm Parkhead; 11.3mm Bridge of Allan; 13.0mm Dunblane).

June. Warm and dry.

For the first 15 days the weather was very settled. The 3rd was rather dull with spells of heavy rain. A north-westerly breeze developed on the 7th which had become gusty by the 9th, and the visibility was excellent in the polar air. The cloud cover moved away on the 11th and the daytime temperature rose under relatively clear skies over the next few days to reach 22.2°C on the 14th (26.9°C Bridge of Allan; 22.0°C Dunblane). The night minimum temperature hovered perilously close to freezing, especially on the 12th, but no frosts were recorded. Rain fell overnight on the 18th/19th and 19th/20th which generated a 48h total of 10.1mm (9.0mm Bridge of Allan; 16.7mm Dunblane). Settled weather became re-established on the 21st and persisted for the remainder of the month. Daytime temperatures consistently topped 20°C, reaching an unbearable 29.2°C on the 29th (34.4°C at the sheltered garden site in Bridge of Allan). Afternoon temperatures were affected by a sea-breeze which also drove the east-coast haar inland.

July. Warm but wet mid-month.

The 1st was sunny and warm after which there were occasional spells of rain over the next few days. From the 8th the weather became sunny and warm in a light ENE breeze. The daytime maximum temperature was consistently above 20°C and reached 23.6°C on the 13th (27.3°C Bridge of Allan; 25.0°C Dunblane). Very heavy thundery rain fell late on the 11th, which amounted to 20.4mm (32.0mm Dunblane) and more thundery showers continued into the 15th. From the 20th the weather was warm but very humid with occasional rain. Brighter weather arrived on the 21st and, as there was very little cloud, and only the slightest of air movement, daytime temperatures began to rise steeply reaching 27.3°C on the 30th (30.0°C Bridge of Allan; 29.5°C Dunblane). Conditions were often sultry and were relieved only occasionally by an afternoon sea-breeze. Cloud increased during the afternoon of the 30th and at 18.30 BST there was a torrential thunderstorm in the Forth valley which brought 13.2mm to Bridge of Allan in less than 30 minutes. However, the storm failed to clear the air and the 31st was again hot and sunny after a misty start.

August. Exceptionally hot and dry.

The daytime maximum temperature exceeded 20°C over the first 25 days, and the total rainfall for the month amounted to only 13.5mm. The first eleven days were hot, sunny and dry, although they occasionally started with mist, which cleared by midday. The average maximum temperature over this period was 24.9°C (26.7°C Bridge of Allan; 24.4°C Dunblane) with 30°C being exceeded in Bridge of Allan on the 2nd, 10th and 11th. The 11th was unpleasantly hot and very humid as cloud increased from the west, and light rain was falling early on the 12th. There was a light SW breeze between the 13th and 15th but temperatures soared again, exceeding 30°C in Bridge of Allan on the 17th and 18th. Cloud increased late on the 18th bringing some rain (7.6mm Parkhead; 7.1mm Bridge of Allan; 9.0mm Craigmill; 3.5mm Dunblane). The weather was exceptionally dull over the next three days with low cloud on the hills and poor visibility. Daytime temperatures continued to top 20°C and the night minimum had only fallen to 16.0°C by the morning of the 19th. A welcome showery westerly airstream arrived on the 22nd which brought unsettled, but fresher, weather until the 26th. A fresh to strong north-westerly breeze then developed which brought about a sharp drop in temperature and the night minimum on the 28th was only 5.5°C (4.7oC Bridge of Allan; 3.5°C Dunblane).

September. Continuing warm, but very wet at times.

The weather remained settled for a while but cloud increased through the day on the 1st and there was heavy overnight rain, which continued all day on the 2nd. The wet weather persisted until the early hours of the 5th and the total rainfall over the first four days amounted to 58.5mm (66.0mm Bridge of Allan; 68.0 Dunblane). General rain on the 7th amounted to a further 19.1mm (22.4mm Bridge of Allan). From the 8th the weather was very changeable with lengthy sunny spells separated by occasionally heavy rain, particularly along the east coast. There were torrential downpours in Aberdeen and along the south coast of the Moray Firth which caused the temporary closure of the Aberdeen to Inverness railway line. Amounts of rain in the Stirling area were, however, relatively small (6.8mm Parkhead; 9.4mm Bridge of Allan). Central Scotland enjoyed three warm and dry days between the 14th and 16th and the temperature reached 20.5°C on the 16th (23.7°C Bridge of Allan). This eventually gave way to long spells of dull grey weather with early morning fog. More rain fell on the 23rd, 25th and 26th after which temperatures began to fall very quickly in a cold and showery polar airstream. As the sky cleared on the 28th the night minimum temperature fell below freezing, the first air and ground frost of the autumn (–0.5°C Parkhead; –2.7°C Bridge of Allan; –3.5°C Dunblane). By the 31st there were squally showers in a freshening south-westerly, which gusted to 50mph at the University.

October. Warm but very wet.

There was heavy cloud and rain over the first six days, some of which fell in heavy showers, then unsettled weather continued until the 19th and the wind was occasionally fresh to strong west to south-west. Tropical air affected the whole of the British Isles on the 8th, which resulted in high temperatures for the time of year. The maximum temperature reached 22.6°C and the minimum had fallen to only 13.2°C by the morning of the 9th. By the evening of the 21st the wind was south-westerly force 7 and was accompanied by heavy rain. Further rain followed on the 22nd bringing the 48h total to 27.1mm (27.2mm Bridge of Allan; 27.5mm Dunblane). On the 24th the wind freshened southerly, reaching gale force by late evening, which resulted in minor storm damage. The maximum gust was 45mph (University). Wet and windy weather continued all day on the 25th and was accompanied by occasional thunder. The bad weather continued unabated into the 26th and flooding became widespread. The 48h rainfall amounted to 56.4mm (55.6mm Bridge of Allan; 52.0mm Dunblane). Calmer, drier, weather returned briefly on the 27th but rain resumed during the afternoon of the 28th. The mean maximum and minimum air temperatures for the month were generally more than 2°C above the long-term averages and no air frosts were registered at Parkhead. While the rainfall in western Scotland was as much as three times the long-term average, it was slightly below average along the east-coast, reflecting the dominance of westerly airflow.

November. Mild but generally dull.

There was a spell of very clear weather with little or no cloud over the first four days. Night temperatures fell sharply, dropping to –0.9°C by the morning of the 4th (–3.2°C Bridge of Allan; –4.0°C Dunblane). The cloud cover increased from the north-west late on the 4th which prevented further frosts, but the calm weather continued until the 10th. Rain began to fall during the evening of the 11th and 11.1mm had fallen by 09.00 GMT on the 12th. Light drizzle then persisted throughout the 12th but generated only 0.2mm in the raingauge. The 13th and 14th were both very dull, with dense fog occuring on the latter.

Temperatures fell very sharply on the 15th in cold polar air, struggling to rise above 5oC on the 16th and 17th and snow fell on higher ground. The snowline was down to 1500 ft (458m) in the Ochil Hills and there was a good cover on the Scottish ski slopes. The night minimum fell to –1.8°C on the 18th (–4.2°C Bridge of Allan; –5.5°C Dunblane). Light rain began to fall during the afternoon of the 20th and, with the air approaching from the south-west, daytime temperatures exceeded 12.0°C from the 21st to the 24th and the snow disappeared from the Ochil Hills. Heavy rain fell in a fresh south-westerly from the afternoon of the 23rd and continued overnight (13.0mm), returning to give another 11.4mm on the 25th.

December. Relatively mild at first but turning exceptionally cold.

Over the first four days the weather was exceptionally dull with only a brief glimpse of the sun on the afternoon of the 3rd. Temperatures were, however, moderately high reaching 11.9°C on the 2nd (12.0°C Bridge of Allan on the 3rd) and falling to only 7.3°C on the 3rd. A cold and moist easterly airstream developed on the 5th which contained rain and sleet, and on the 8th to 12th fog persisted for much of the day. On the 8th, freezing fog restricted the daytime temperature to a maximum –0.8°C (–1.0°C Bridge of Allan; –1.5°C Dunblane). From the 13th to the 16th a dull and raw easterly breeze affected much of Britain. When the cloud cleared, minimum temperatures dropped very quickly to –7.6°C on the 21st (–10.0°C Bridge of Allan; –13.5°C Dunblane). By the early afternoon of the 21st there was a heavy fall of snow which had gradually turned to rain by 09.00 GMT on the 22nd. Cold air spread from the north-east on the 23rd and very heavy snow fell overnight. The wind strengthened, whipping the snow into substantial drifts in exposed places. Shetland was badly affected as a 35cm fall drifted in a north-easterly gale, blocking roads and bringing down power lines. By Christmas Day the worst of the snow had passed and a combination of clear skies, arctic air, and snow-covered ground resulted in temperatures falling to their lowest levels since the winter of 1981-82. Air temperatures at Parkhead (1), Bridge of Allan (2) and Dunblane (3) were –

	Max.			Min.		
	(1)	(2)	(3)	(1)	(2)	(3)
Tuesday 26th	–4.0	–1.0	–1.0	–8.6	–10.7	–10.5
Wednesday 27th	–6.7	–5.6	–7.5	–13.5	–15.0	–13.5
Thursday 28th	–6.0	–4.2	–7.5	–13.1	–15.6	–13.0

By midday on the 29th the air temperature in Bridge of Allan had risen to only –6.8°C and patchy freezing fog began to develop during the afternoon, but there was a remarkable rise in temperature by the morning of the 30th. By the afternoon rain had begun to fall (10.5mm) and there was a rapid thaw. The rapidity of the rise in temperature caused water pipes to burst and many saw in the New Year to the sound of cascading water.

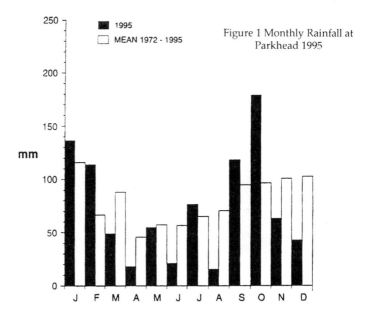

Figure 1 Monthly Rainfall at Parkhead 1995

NOTES

Hot summer 1995

The weather statistics for Parkhead show how remarkably hot and dry the months June, July and August were. The maximum temperature was 20.0°C or better on no fewer than 60 days, and topped 25°C on 18 days. The average daily maximum temperature was 21.3°C, 2.4oC higher than the long-term average and the total rainfall was 109mm, 58% of average. There were three rainless spells lasting 11 days, these being 5th to 15th June, 21st June to 1st July, and 31st July to 10th August. Over the United Kingdom as a whole, the 3-month period was the second driest, the third hottest and the fifth sunniest since records began. August was not only the hottest and sunniest August on record but was the hottest month ever recorded. There were, of course, regional differences within the UK which depended on the surface pressure patterns. The average sea-level pressure for June and August was high to the west and south-west of the British Isles. This tended to favour the west coast in terms of the duration of bright sunshine. In contrast, pressure was high to the south-east in July which tended to favour the east coast. Comparisons have obviously been made with the hot and very dry summer of 1976 and the general view would appear to be that 1995 was the better summer in Scotland and Wales, but inferior in England.

Although the hot weather was a bonus for the tourist industry, heavy prices

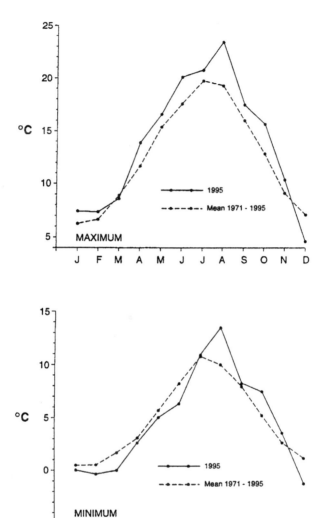

Figure 2 Air Temperatures at Parkhead 1995

were paid in terms of acute shortages of water, discomfort for asthma and hayfever sufferers, and alarmingly high levels of traffic-related pollution in larger towns and cities. By early August public warnings of very poor air quality were being issued and some attempts were made to regulate urban traffic. The lack of water had a severe effect on wildlife. Glue (1995) reports that "... falling water levels in lakes and rivers led to late nests of diving duck, moorhen, dipper and wagtail falling to predators; ... certain thrush, finch and warbler nests were left exposed by premature leaf-fall and desiccated ground vegetation". There was also a shortage of small rodents on which birds of prey could feed.

Exceptionally mild October

'Exceptional' seems to have been an apt description for the air temperature during a number of autumn months in recent years. Temperatures have not been decimal points above the long-term average but a matter of 2 or 3°C greater. The October 1995 averages were more than 2°C above average throughout Western Europe. Such very mild spells of weather in middle latitudes are associated with warm air advection from lower latitudes. While this raises the temperature it can also energise mid-latitude depressions bringing strong winds and heavy rain along western coasts, which was certainly the case during October, as is indicated by the high rainfall figures in western Scotland and the gales in the latter half of the month. Whether such spells of weather are, in any way, related to global warming is by no means clear but during recent years there has been a trend towards a higher frequency of westerly maritime weather patterns during the winter half-year, at the expense of colder and drier easterly continental types.

Two spells of cold weather in December

Two relatively brief cold spells with frost and snow occurred during December which together provide useful examples of the contrasting origins of this type of winter weather. The first occurred between the 4th and 8th as a strong anticyclone became centred over Scandinavia. This brought cold continental air in an easterly breeze in which there were spells of sleet. Once the cloud cleared, night temperatures fell below freezing. When this type of weather pattern persists over a longer period the air which reaches the British Isles may have its origins in the Siberian winter anticyclone and can be exceptionally cold. The second cold spell began early on Christmas Eve and resulted from the arrival of arctic maritime air from the north. Thus 'the north wind doth blow ...' and heavy snow fell giving not only the heaviest December snowfall for 50 years (Met Office) but also a White Christmas. The snow had mostly stopped by Christmas Day but as the clouds cleared away the temperature fell to their lowest since December 1981, reversing the recent trend towards warmer winter months. The frost was penetrating and minimum temperatures fell to −16.9°C in Bridge of Allan, well short of the −27.0°C registered at Altnaharra in Highland Region, which was a new UK record low for December. The full impact of the cold has yet to be determined but at the time of writing it had claimed at least eleven lives and payments of cold weather social benefit allowances were made over much of Scotland. *Railnews* reported that "Trains were knocked out as air systems froze, seizing up compressors, brakes, doors and control gear" and post Christmas rail services in central Scotland were reduced to less than half. ScotRail estimated that damage to trains had cost £300 000. The rapidity of the thaw over New Year caused many burst pipes and the resulting damage and insurance claims will take many weeks to process. The absence of winds from the west created a precipitation anomaly along the west coast of Scotland which received very little during December, causing localised water shortages.

The above notes have been compiled with the assistance of material from Outlook (Met Office), Railnews and Weather Log (Royal Meteorological Society).

Forth Valley Frost Hollow

Cold air tends to drain *katabatically* into the Forth Valley which means that there is a greater risk of frost over the lower-lying ground, commonly referred to as the *frost-hollow effect*. A comparison has been made between frequencies of air frosts at Bridge of Allan (10m) and Parkhead (35m) which illustrates this increased risk.

Monthly mean air-frost frequencies at Bridge of Allan and Parkhead 1988-1995

	Parkhead	Bridge of Allan
January	9.4	11.8
February	10.5	10.0
March	6.6	8.4
April	2.9	5.8
May	0.9	2.1
June	0.0	0.1
July	0.0	0.0
August	0.0	0.0
September	0.1	1.0
October	1.9	4.4
November	6.8	10.0
December	11.6	13.8
YEAR	50.6	67.3

New Parkhead Climatological Station

During 1993 the University of Stirling intimated its intention to construct new residences on the nursery site which would have affected the observations at Parkhead, so plans were put in hand to move the station to a new site. The University agreed that this could be located in the Memorial Garden, between the existing site and Alexander Court (residences) (Figure 3). In order to ensure continuity of the observational record it was decided that old and new stations should be operated in parallel over nine months during 1995. The new station, called Parkhead II, was installed on December 14th 1994

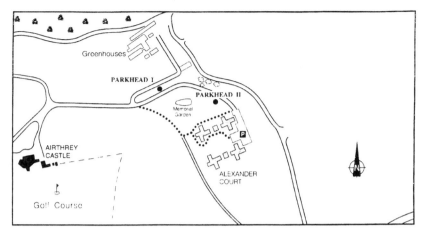

Figure 3 Location of Parkhead Climatological stations.

and formal observation began on January 1st 1995. Parallel operation was maintained until September 30th 1995 and Parkhead I was dismantled on October 25th. The new site is slightly more exposed than the old, which has been reflected in the observations. Statistical comparisons between the daily records for the two sites indicate, as expected, a high degree of association but, in summary:-

(i)   For maximum temperatures in excess of 20°C Parkhead I tended to be warmer while for low maxima (<5°C) the reverse was the case
(ii) Minimum temperatures tended to be higher at Parkhead II
(iii) Rainfall at Parkhead II was very slightly higher

A homogeneous record of daily temperature and rainfall for Parkhead I will continue to be generated using the following regression equations:-

Parkhead $I_{MAXTEMP}$ = −0.379 + 1.023 Parkhead $II_{MAXTEMP}$

Parkhead $I_{MINTEMP}$ = −0.183 + 0.954 Parkhead $II_{MINTEMP}$

Parkhead I_{RAIN} = 0.994 Parkhead II_{RAIN}

Additional weather records

Data from an additional source have been helpful in compiling this report. Neil Bielby's records come from his garden in Ochiltree, Dunblane, which is to the east of the Dunblane Hydro. Despite the very different exposures and types of instruments the records show a good level of agreement with Parkhead and Bridge of Allan. If any reader of this report takes regular **daily** readings of temperature and rainfall, plus any other meteorological observations, and would like to consider their inclusion in the 1996 issue of the Bulletin, would they please contact the author, giving details of the site and the nature of the measurements taken. We are particularly interested in records from the Forth Valley and Strathallan.

Local Rainfall Network

The Stirling area has a long history of rainfall recording and at the turn of the Century Colonel Stirling of Gargunnock House was collating rainfall records for publication in the *Transactions of the Stirling Natural History and Archaeological Society* (Harrison 1980). **Anybody who may be interested in re-establishing a network covering the Forth, Teith and Devon catchments and Strathallan** is invited to contact the author who will be happy to provide details on how to embark on rainfall recording using very basic equipment. It is anticipated that contributors would agree to submit regular returns of their monthly rainfall totals.

References

Glue, D. E. 1995 The combined influences of the mild 1994/95 winter and the protracted hot dry summer on Britain's breeding birds in 1995 *Journal of Meteorology* (UK) 20 (203) 339-342.

Harrison S. J. (1980) Rainfall in the Stirling area *Forth Naturalist & Historian* 5, 23-34.

Acknowledgement

This paper is based on the more comprehensive *Annual Climatological Bulletin* No. 17, available in the University library and purchasable from Climate Services, Environmental Sciences Department.

FORTH AREA BIRD REPORT 1995

C J Henty
University of Stirling

A record number of contributors appear this year. Notable records for this year include winter Iceland Gull and Great Grey Shrike, a spring Red-backed Shrike, an autumn Sabine's Gull, a small wreck of Little Auks, and several Smew and Marsh Harriers. There was a fair autumn passage of Curlew Sandpipers and Ruffs whilst in spring Turtle Dove, Yellow Wagtail, and Lesser Whitethroat all appeared in possible breeding habitats though with no indications of nesting. Stonechats have increased, though possibly only to be hit by the severe frost in December. This report is compiled from a larger archive of records submitted to the local recorder under the national scheme organised by the Scottish Ornithologists Club. The area covered by the report comprises the council areas of Falkirk and Clackmannan together with Stirling, excluding Loch Lomondside and other parts of the Clyde drainage basin. Please note that we do not include the Endrick water, i.e Fintry and Balfron. Records from Carron Valley may be published both here and in the report on Clyde birds. The inland part of Falkirk continues to receive reasonable attention, the extensive and often inaccessable hill area in the north of our area has had only sporadic coverage.

The SOC has pressed for a more systematic vetting of records of species that are unusual locally, this area now has an informal panel of five - C. Henty (Recorder), W. Brackenridge (Dep. Recorder), J. Crook (local SOC rep), A. Blair and D. Thorogood. The judging of national UK or Scottish rarities continues as before, but we have produced for the upper Forth a list of species that are scarce locally and where the records need to be supported by either a full description or sufficient evidence to remove any reasonable doubt. This list and a background explanation have been circulated to a hard core of observers and can be got from the recorder at SOC meetings or by post. Any species which is a vagrant to the area, and most of those which are asterisked in this report, will come into this category.

There are a few changes in the format of the species account this year. Where there are a number of records about arrival or departure of summer migrants, I have summarised these in a separate section before the "county" locality paragraphs. Records from previous years have been added at the end of a species section in different print and marked with the year, whilst those species that are fairly certainly escapes (though sometimes breeding ferally elsewhere) have been put together at the end of the main species list. This is meant to emphasise to contributors that there are a number of birds at large that may not be in the field guides but are worth recording. Finally, I have changed the naming of some carse localities where the map name states

"Moss" but the birds are certainly on farmland. Thus Drip Carse refers to the farmland between Craigforth and Chalmerston, Blairdrummond Carse is between Ochtertyre and Coldoch, and Thornhill Carse is west of Coldoch to the edge of Flanders Moss.

The 1995 weather provided a series of extreme conditions. January started with snow but was then unsettled with strong winds. The first half of February brought floods, leading to a brief spell of frost and sun in the last week, whilst March was cold and snowy with an Arctic airstream. By contrast April was warm and very dry except for brief snow in the third week. May was unremarkable, apart for some snow on the 12th, but June was warm and dry. July and August were very warm, usually above 20° and reaching 30° occasionally; there was little rain except for heavy , thundery bursts in mid July. Both September and October were warmer than usual, but about 50% wetter. Early November was calm but it was cold with snow on high ground in the third week; this led to warmer, wet weather persisting into early December. However, after dull but bleak conditions in mid-December there was heavy snow and gales whilst clear skies after Christmas caused very severe night frosts and day temperatures that often failed to reach -5°C, hoar frost stayed on the trees even after hours of bright sun and many rivers froze.

Most information on the breeding numbers of common species come from two studies of mapped territories. One is a Common Birds Census plot east of Doune, this is 87 Ha of undulating, dry-field farmland at about 70 m a.s.l, mixed pasture and winter cereal, which is referred to as "Doune CBC" in text. The other is a Waterways Birds Survey along 5 km of the R.Devon at Alva which has much damp scrub surrounded by mixed pasture and arable, referred to as "Devon WBS", or, for species that are not fully mapped, as "5 km of lower Devon". For less common species I can sometimes mention data in terms of the numbers of pairs or apparently occupied territories for particular locations. Several observers send in an extensive list for their home locality, much of this information is not appropriate for these annual reports but it is valuable to have on record and I am keeping them in a special file. I am working on some suggestions as to how such lists could be made more systematic and comparable amongst each other.

For many species the records sent in are very unrepresentative of their general distribution, this applies particularly to very common species or to those that are secretive or breed in inaccessible places. Readers can consult the the Check List published in the *Forth Naturalist and Historian* vol 15, but in addition I have in this report put, after the species name, a coded summary of general distribution - which often apparently contradicts the detailed records that are published for the year.

B - Breeding status, widespread (in more than five 10 km squares)
b -   "   "   , local , scarce (in fewer than five 10 km squares)
W - Winter status, widespread or often in groups of more than ten.
w -   "   "   , local, scarce (local and usually fewer than ten in a group)
P - Passage (used when species is usually absent in winter, P or p used for

widespread or local as in winter status)

S or s - a few species are present in summer but do not normally breed.

Thus BW would be appropriate for Robin, B for Swallow, p for Ruff and SW for Cormorant. No status letter is used if a species occurs less than every other year.

An asterix (*) in front of the species name means that all records received have been quoted.

For several species of waders and duck more information has been received than can be sensibly reported in full detail. In these cases I have mentioned the more striking individual records and summarised the rest for each month or half-month as the minimum number of birds that can reasonably account for the records, this means adding up the maximum numbers recorded for what I take to be distinct localities. These "Area summaries" clearly have limitations, underestimating when an important locality has not been visited and overestimating if the same flock has been reported from two places that I have assumed to be separate; however, this is the best way of giving a more systematic description of the seasonal pattern of occurrence. Neil Bielby, the organiser for the inland waters part of the national wildfowl counts (WEBS), has made available an account of the results for the winter 1995-1996. These often contribute to the species accounts and there is also a separate summary at the end of the report which concentrates on localities.

With increasing amounts of information coming in more help would be welcome in entering the observers' notes into a basic database and in assessing these in the case of heavily recorded species; also a comprehensive gazetteer of localities and their map locations would be very useful - any volunteers?

The following abbreviations have been used : AoT - apparently occupied territory, BoA - Bridge of Allan, c/n - clutch of n eggs, CBC- Common Birds Census, CP - Country Park, F - Female, GP - gravel pit, J - juvenile, L. - Loch, NR - Nature Reserve, M - Male, ON - on nest, Res - Reservoir, SP - summer plumage, V - Valley, WBS- Waterways Bird Survey, WG - Wildlife Garden, Y - young.

This report has been compiled from records submitted by: B D Allan, P&M Ashworth, A Ayre, B W Barker, A van Beist, M V Bell, N Bielby, Birdline Scotland, A Blair, W R Brackenridge, R A Broad, W Brown, D M Bryant, G Bryson, M Callan, D A Christie, K Dodds, A Downie, W McEwan, P R Gordon, B Hay, C J Henty, T Jacobs, E A Jardine, D&R Jones, A Maciver, A K McNeil, J Mitchell, G Owens, D Orr-Ewing, D J Price, J Pulleyn, H M Rankine, H Robb, P W Sandeman, S Sankey, R Shand, T D Smith, M Steward (Forest Enterprise), P Stirling-Aird, B R Thompson, D Thorogood, J Towill, M Trubridge, J Wheeler, I Wilson.

Thanks are due to the Deputy Recorder, W.R.Brackenridge, for assistance and advice on records, to Dr S.J.Harrison for a copy of the *Annual Climatological Bulletin* (1995), to P.Stirling -Aird for data from the Raptor Study Group, and to Dr M.V. Bell for assessing the counts of geese.

SYSTEMATIC LIST

Codes - F and C indicate records from Falkirk and Clackmannan, S and SWP those from one time Stirlingshire and south-west Perthshire parts of Stirling.

RED-THROATED DIVER *Gavia stellata (b,w)*
2 Loch A 6 May. 2 Loch C 24 Apr. 2 Loch D 22 Jun, absent 22 Jul. 2 Loch E 23 May to 26 Jun (no successful nesting). 2 Loch I 21 Apr (WRB JM).
F   4 Blackness 25 Jan (RS). 16 records Skinflats -Carriden 18 Nov to 20 Dec, max 4 Kinneil on 3 Dec (DT AB DMB MVB WRB).
C   1 Alloa Inch 22 Nov (CJH).
1994:   2 dead, unoiled, Blackness -Dunmore in Feb-Mar (PRG).

BLACK-THROATED DIVER *Gavia arctica (b,w)*
    Pair Loch A 21 Mar, 2 pairs 18 Apr to 14 Jun, 3 on 18 Jul - 1Y reared at 2nd attempt. Pair with nest Loch F 26 May to10 Jul, no Y hatched. 2 Loch G 21 Mar, 1 on 18 Jul (BDA NB WRB DAC).
F   2 Blackness 25 Jan & 1 on 18 Nov; 2 Carriden 9 Dec (DMB CJH RS).

LITTLE GREBE *Tachybaptus ruficollis (B,w)*
F   3 Grangemouth Docks 15 Jan; 1 Kinneil 28 Oct (BDA MVB). 10 (some juvs) Drumbowie Res 4 Sep (NB).
C   5 pairs reared 4Y at Gartmorn, 24 on 10 Sep (MC).
S   lst Airthrey 26 Feb (KD), 2 Pairs fledged 4Y (MVB). Pair bred Carron Valley Res (AKM). 1 N.Third Res 2 Nov (CJH).
SWP   In breeding season (Mar-Sep) at L Arklet, Menteith Hills, Hutchison Dam, Gart Loch, Arivurichardich Res, L.Lubnaig, L.Voil, L.Dochart, L.Iubhair. In Nov-Dec at Kippen, L.Watston, Cambusmore, L.Dochart & L.Lubnaig (8 during severe frost on 27 Dec). 1 Ochlochy Pond on 27 Oct, lst record (NB WRB AC CJH PWS SS).

GREAT CRESTED GREBE *Podiceps cristatus (b,W)*
F   4 Black Loch 27 Mar (2 displaying), 7 adults on 4 Sep & 3 on 6 Oct (NB). Kinneil: 29 on 1 Jan, 51 on 26 Feb, 7 on 6 Mar, 2 on 8 Apr, 2 on 27 May. 4 on 16 Jul & 27 on 28th, 40 on 9 Aug, 67 on 10 Sep, 40 on 7 Oct, 55 on 11 Dec (AB DMB DT). 12 Blackness 2 Jan, 46 on 13 Sep & 25 on 7 Oct (AB CJH DT). 18 Carriden 9 Dec (DMB).
    1994: 5 dead, unoiled, Blackness -Dunmore in Feb-Mar (PRG).
C   Pair at Gartmorn unsuccessful (MC).
S   Carron V Res: 1st on 12 Mar, 3 pairs on 25th & 7 on 9 Apr; all failed due to falling water level. Last 2 on 7 Nov (BDA DAC NB AKM DT). 2 L.Coulter 27 Apr & 1 on 4 Sep (BDA NB).
SWP   In breeding season at L.Rusky, L.Watston, L.Ard, L.Venachar, Lake of Menteith (Juv seen Sep-Oct), Quarry Loch (3 juv in Sep) (BDA NB CJH JM JT).

SLAVONIAN GREBE *Podiceps auritus*
1994 :   1 dead, unoiled, Blackness -Dunmore in Feb-Mar (PRG).

FULMAR *Fulmarus glacialis (p)*
F   1 Blackness 5 Mar. Skinflats-Kinneil: 1 on 28 May, total 18 from 10 Aug to 3 Sep (BDA AB GO DT).

MANX SHEARWATER *Puffinus puffinus*
F   1 Grangemouth 26 Aug (DT).

GANNET *Sula bassana (p)*
F   All records of immatures - 1 Grangemouth on 17 Sep & 2 Kinneil on 22nd; 1 Skinflats on 28 Oct - walking on mudflats with goose flock (GO DT).

CORMORANT *Phalacrocorax carbo (S,W)*
Forth Estuary: 293 on 15 Jan (DMB)
F   Skinflats max 81 on 15 Jan, 103 on 22 Oct & 117 on 9 Dec (MVB). 19 Kennetpans 15 Jan & 135 on 31 Dec (CJH).
C   S.Alloa roost: 15 on 10 Jul & 105 on 20 Sep (WRB CJH).
S   11 Carron Valley Res 22 Dec (NB TDS). 10 Airthrey 19 Mar (KD).
SWP   5 Lake of Menteith 21 Feb & 17 on 26 Nov. 13 L.Lubnaig 28 Nov (NB).
1994:   4 dead, unoiled, Blackness -Dunmore in Feb-Mar. 1 ringed Little Ross (Dumfries) on 13 Jun 1992 -"died trying to swallow salmon" (PRG).

SHAG *Phalacrocorax aristotelis (w)*
1994:   8 dead, unoiled, Blackness -Dunmore in Feb-Mar. 2 ringed Isle of May: 1 on 21 Jun 1981, 1 on 22 Jun 1992 (PRG).

GREY HERON *Ardea cinerea (B,W)*
F   Max Skinflats 13 on 22 Oct & 15 on 9 Dec (MVB).
C   4 nests Gartmornhill (MC). Max 6 Carron Valley Res 4 Dec (NB).
S   20 BoA 11 Oct (KD).
SWP   27 used nests Blairdrummond (Nyadd) 15 May. 19 L.Venachar 25 Oct & 14 Nov (NB CJH). 8 Lecropt 7 Jan & 16 Dec (MVB). 15 Daldorn 8 Oct, 6 Torrie Loch 12 Nov (BWB).

MUTE SWAN *Cygnus olor (B,W)*
F   Pair + 5Y Callendar Park 11 Jun (BDA). Pair + 3Y Little Denny Res 4 Sep (NB). 11 Carronshore 14 & 30 Sep (AB). Max Skinflats 5 on 28 Oct & Kinneil 5 on 27 Aug (GO DT). 8 -> N, Dunmore 9 Sep (GB).
C   Gartmorn: Pair reared 7Y; 71 on 30 Sep, 61 on 15 Oct & 45 on 18 Dec (MC CJH). 2 nests & 4 imm at Cambus on 15 Apr , 1 pair reared 5 Y (BDA CJH). 1 AoT, no nest , on Devon WBS (CJH). 20 Manor Powis in Jan & 18 Mar (WRB NB).
S   Pair at Airthrey reared 8 out of 9Y (MVB). 33 Kildean 4 May (CJH).
SWP   Pairs with juv seen in Sep at Cromlix Lodge & Cullings Pond (NB). 22 Lake of Menteith 21 & 26 Mar (RAB NB).

WHOOPER SWAN *Cygnus cygnus (W)*
WEBS max total of 90 in Nov (NB)
F   Skinflats: 6 on 8 Jan, 1 ad with neckband - tagged Iceland in Aug 1984; 8 -> N over Carron 11 Mar (AB); 8 on 28 Oct (GO). 5 L.Ellrig 8 Jan (TDS), 6 Bonnybridge 4 Feb (AA).

C   Gartmorn: 8 on 2 Jan; 3 on 30 Sep & 12 on 18 Dec (WB MC CJH). 31
     Menstrie on 4 Jan & 23 on 9th (BRT). 1 on Devon 8 April (CJH). 1 (ad
     with yellow ring) Tullibody Inch 26 Aug (DMB).
S   10 Arnprior 2 Mar, 9 Kippen 9 Dec (CJH MT). 7 Carron Valley Res &
     10 on 4 Dec (NB WME TDS). 5 -> E over Stirling 26 Oct (DT), 3 swans
     immensely high and descending over Kippen on 28th were
     presumably Whoopers arriving (CJH).
SWP 24 Lecropt Carse 4 Feb (AD). Drip carse: 48 from 4 to 25 Mar - 3 ad
     with neck bands had been tagged in Iceland in 1994 (DAC DT IW);
     autumn max 55 on 30 Nov which roosted on Forth 200m away (CJH).
     18 Thornhill 11 Feb, 11 L.Katrine 2 Apr & 10 Lake of Menteith 7 Apr
     (CJH MT DT). 25 L.Dochart14 Feb, 14 on 14 Mar & 20 on 21 Nov; 26
     Killin on 27 Dec (NB PWS). 11 L.Lubnaig 27 Dec and smaller numbers
     on L.Iubhair, Balvag, L.Katrine, L.Arklet, L.Ard, L.Venachar, L.Ruskie,
     Torrie Loch, L.Ruskie, L. Chip Dhuibh, L.Lairig Cheile (NB BWB DAC
     BH MT).

PINK-FOOTED GOOSE *Anser brachyrhynchus (W)*
The Pinkfeet and Greylag Geese data have been summarised by Dr M V Bell, with
additions by the Editor, from records of many observers; the main counters were
MVB, DMB, MC, NB, SS, MT.

After heavy snow further north, on 28 Jan 7780 were feeding in the
Forth valley between Blairdrummond Moss and the M9. There were
also 1000 at Tullibody Inch on 2 Feb. These birds had dispersed a
fortnight later and numbers in the Forth valley were low for the
remainder of the winter. Only 240 were at Lake of Menteith on 9 Apr
(though 800 on 13th); the 1085 feeding east of Thornhill to the M9,
and 2000 at Blairdrummond in late March, were thought to have
flighted from Strathallan. There were also 2300 at Alloa Inch on 9 Apr
and 3000 on 14th with the last being 40 on 13 May. Numbers inland
in Falkirk are usually low, eg 126 near Slamannan on 21 Jan. Visible
spring departures include 308 NW over Cambus and 55 E over
Aberfoyle on 14 May.

In autumn 1995 the two main arrival days were 24 and 28 Sept, when
skeins flew S over Alloa Inch and Gartmorn Dam; however, some
birds overshot and returned north, eg 85 over Dunblane on evening
of the 24th. The mid-October count found 3070 Skinflats, 600
L.Mahaick, 1742 L.Rusky and 2169 Lake of Menteith. The total had
decreased by late November with the count on 26th locating 2000 at
Skinflats, 41 Alloa Inch, 404 L.Rusky and 2801 at Lake of Menteith, but
none at L.Mahaick. This site has become considerably less important
in the last few autumns. Following the very clean cereal harvest, a few
geese from Carsebreck were commuting into the Forth valley by the
second week of October, with larger numbers from mid-November.
In the severe weather at the end of the year there were 4930 between
Blairdrummond Moss and Lecropt on 28 Dec.

BEAN GOOSE *Anser fabalis (W)*
F   65 Slamannan 7 Jan & 132 on 10th; average flock size 63 in Jan and 70 in Feb, last 27 on 2 Mar (AMcI TDS). 44 L.Ellrig 14 Oct (AMcI), 43 Slamannan 22 Oct (GO).
S   15 Carron V Res 1 Oct , 33 on 8th & 15th (NB AMcI DT).

WHITE-FRONTED GOOSE *Anser albifrons (w)*
F   6 (Greenland form) Slamannan 19 Feb, 1 on 20th. 2 Skinflats 27 Oct (AD GO).
SWP   1 (Greenland form) Lecropt 21 Jan (MVB).

GREYLAG GOOSE *Anser anser* (b,W)
Numbers in the Forth valley were lower than in the last couple of winters and most birds were in the Gargunnock-Drip area, with the Thornhill-Kippen area much less important than a few years ago. 760 were on the carse on 29 Jan and 850 on 9 Apr, but there were individual site records of 800 at Plean on 1 Jan and 830 Gargunnock on 13 Mar. In Falkirk there were 650 on the Slamannan plateau on 13 Jan and 150 on 4 Feb, with 250 at Blackness on 5 Mar. 60 flying NW over Menstrie on 8 Apr and 50 on the 15th were probably migrating. One or two birds, probably injured, were at Kinneil lagoon from 29 Jan to 26 Oct. 1 at L.Katrine on 10 Jun may well have been breeding.
In autumn numbers were even lower with 100 Lake of Menteith and 29 L.Rusky on 15 Oct, 270 Gargunnock area on 19 Nov and 103 Callendar area on 28 Nov. At Stronend on 28 Oct 30 flew steadily W. However, outwith the main counts there were 800 at Blairdrummond on 28 Nov, 100 Cambusmore on 30 Nov, 100 Killin on 2 Dec and 150 Kennetpans on 3 Dec. A flock of 600 at Gartmore on 31 Oct was rather unexpected and birds may be being missed in the west of the area - there were 93 at L.Venachar on 14 Nov. Substantial flocks also occur around Avonbridge, 650 on 13 Jan and 200 on 13 Nov. In Perthshire birds are retreating westwards away from the the more intensively farmed arable areas and the commercial shooting parties. Perhaps the same is happening here. The hard weather at the year end brought 950 to the east end of the carse on 28 Dec. Gartmorn had 42 on 15 Oct; none roosted there on 26 Nov but 360 were found feeding near Alloa.

CANADA GOOSE *Branta canadensis (b)*
WEBS season total almost double 1994-5 (NB).
C   11 Gartmorn 30 Sept, 4 Oct-Dec (PMA WB MC CJH)
S   29 Airthrey 5 Sep (MVB). 30 Carron Valley Res 15 Oct (AMcI DT).
SWP   4 Lake of Menteith 30 Mar (DT); 11 L.Mahaick 10 Mar & 8 on 25 Apr (NB DOE); 3 L.Ard 21 May (BDA). Pair + 5Y Hutchison Dam 3 Sep (WRB); 7 L.Watston 9 Sep (CJH). 2 ->W Dunblane 24 May. 26 Blairdrummond 27 Jan, 38 on 27 Oct & 30 on 22 Dec - typical of 1995 numbers (NB). A small dark bird with Pinkfeet at Lecropt 28 Jan (MVB) and Blairdrummond carse 19 Mar (DT) *(possibly a nearctic migrant, Ed)*.

BARNACLE GOOSE *Branta leucopsis (w)*
F   6 L.Ellrig 2 Oct (AMcI). 6 Kinneil 7 Oct (AB), 90 on 8th left S (DT);
      Skinflats: 7 on 2 Oct, 30 on 10th, 105 on 19th, 43 on 22nd & 60 on 28th
      (AB DMB MVB CJH GO RS).
C   2 Alloa Inch 9 & 14 Apr (DMB).
S   1 Carron Valley Res 1 Oct & 2 with Bean Geese on 15th (AMcI DT). 23
      L.Coulter 9 Oct (NB).
SWP   2 Thornhill 6 Apr & 1 on 15th (SS). 1 Lecropt 28 & 29 Jan & 25 Nov
      (MVB AD DT)

BRENT GOOSE *Branta bernicla*
F   1 Kinneil 1 Aug (RS DT) - *odd date, possibly summered (Ed).*

SHELDUCK *Tadorna tadorna (b,W)*
660 Forth Estuary 15 Jan & 3955 on 10 Sep (DMB)
F   Kinneil: 330 on 1 Apr, 29Y seen on 27 May (AB CJH); 5720 on 1
      Aug,1600 on 13 Sep, 500 on 9 Dec (DMB WRB CJH). Skinflats: 406 on
      15 Jan, 152 on 12 Feb, 30 on 28 May, 192 on pool 14 Jul; 1480 on 10 &
      17 Sep,780 on 22 Oct, 65 on 9 Dec (AB MVB CJH GO). Max 5 over
      Dunmore Wood in summer (GB).
C   120 Tullibody Inch 2 Feb, 25 on 10 Jul, 210 on 25 Aug & 40 on 20 Sep
      (DMB WRB CJH). 1 Gartmorn 2 Apr (WB), 2 pairs on Devon WBS 9-
      24 May (CJH)

WIGEON *Anas penelope (b,W)*
940 Forth Estuary 12 Feb & 554 on12 Dec (DMB). WEBS totals increased from
102 in Dec to 2066 in Dec (NB).
F   Kinneil: 550 on 8 Jan & 250 on 6 Mar; 6 on 9 Sep,115 on 8 Oct, 269 on
      18 Nov, & 400 on 23 Dec (AB CJH GO DT). Skinflats: 119 on 9 Sep &
      95 on 22 Oct (AB MVB). 250 Blackness 7 Oct & 153 Carriden on 22nd
      (AB DMB).
C   120 Alloa Inch 9 Apr & 75 on 20 Sep (WRB DMB). 1150 Gartmorn 18
      Dec (MC).
S   160 Craigforth 29 Jan 7 & 80 on 28 Dec (MVB). 104 L.Laggan 22 Jan,
      156 L.Coulter 13 Dec (NB).
SWP   Max Gart Lochs (Cambusmore) Jan-Mar was 275 on 14 Mar, 32 on 19
      Sep & 231 on 22 Dec(NB).

*GADWALL *Anas strepera*
F   M Skinflats 22-28 Oct (BDA AB MVB GO). 1 Kinneil 19 Nov (AB).
C   Pair Gartmorn Sep-Oct (MC).
SWP   2 Doune Ponds 13 Aug (AD).

TEAL *Anas crecca (B,W)*
703 Forth Estuary 15 Jan & 614 on 9 Dec (DMB)
F   Skinflats: 272 on 15 Jan; 4 on 12 Jul & 100 on 7 Dec (AB MVB GO). 45
      Grangemouth 12 Aug & 262 on 22 Oct (DMB DT). Kinneil: 200 on 2
      Jan, 46 as late as 23 Apr; 190 on 12 Dec (AB CJH DT). 12 Larbert Hosp.
      Loch 13 Dec was only 2nd inland WEBS record in Falkirk (NB). 12 on

Avon at Slamannan 6 Mar (TDS).
C   164 Kennetpans 15 Jan. 300 Tullibody Inch 2 Feb (CJH). 205 Gartmorn
     18 Dec (MC).
S   60 Carron Valley Res 12 Sep & 150 on 15 Oct (AKM DT). 34 L.Laggan
     22 Jan & 32 on 11 Dec. 27 L.Coulter 13 Dec was lst WEBS record (NB).
SWP 210 L.Macanrie 22 Jan, 160 on 19 Feb; 80 on 10 Dec (DT). 36 Lake of
     Menteith 21 Mar. 136 L.Ard 15 Dec. 84 Coustry (Blairdrummond) 27
     Oct. 43 L.Dochart 28 Nov (NB). 30 Killin 8 Dec (PWS). 12 L.Dhu
     (Rusky)15 Apr was only record likely to refer to breeding (DT).

MALLARD *Anas platyrhynchos (B,W)*
  1268 Forth Estuary on 16 Jan & 789 on 13 Aug (DMB). On 67 WEBS (inland)
  sites present at all but one; comprises half of all wildfowl with monthly
  average of 3062, slightly greater than last season (NB).
F   Skinflats: 266 on 15 Jan, 200 on 12 Feb; 132 on 13 Aug to 290 on 9 Dec
     (MVB CJH). Kinneil: 300 on 2 Jan, 79 on 8 Jun; 130 on 23 Jul to 300 on
     11 Dec (AB BDA DT). 45 L.Ellrig 8 Jan (TDS).
C   386 Gartmorn 15 Oct (MC). 100 on Devon below Tillicoultry 8 Feb. 18
     AoT on Devon WBS (CJH).
S   372 Airthrey 19 Jan & 394 on 13 Sep; 38 pairs in spring, early broods
     failed but many fledged from later broods (MVB). 96 Touch Res 14
     Feb (IW). Max Carron Valley Res only 88 in Nov (NB).
SWP 250 L.Watston 9 Sep (CJH). Considerable numbers occur on flight
     ponds where duck are fed: four ponds north of Doune held 217, 371,
     201 & 352 in Sep-Nov (NB).106 Doune Ponds 9 Sep (AD). 324 Coustry
     ponds 8 Sep, 310 Blairdrummond Safari Park 24 Nov,122 Ochlochy 30
     Nov. 208 L.Ard 22 Nov & 294 L.Venachar on 28th were highest WEBS
     counts (NB). 200 L.Dochart 13 Dec, 200 Gart Lochs 1 Nov (PWS).

PINTAIL *Anas acuta (W)*
F   Skinflats: max 85 on 15 Jan & 57 on 25 Nov (MVB GO), earlier
     departure this year with lower numbers in March. Noticeable arrival
     in several localities on 10 Sept. Small numbers at Kinneil (as usual)
     except for 15 on 28 Oct (BDA).
C   Pair Cambus 22 Mar & 7 Apr (WRB CJH), 2 Tullibody Inch 14 Sep
     (DMB). 2 Gartmorn Oct-Dec with 3 on 15 Oct (MC).
SWP 2 on Forth at Drip Carse 8 Oct (NB).

Area Summary

Jan	Feb	Mar	Apr	-	Aug	Sep	Oct	Nov	Dec
85	74	31	2		1	17	38	59	58

*GARGANEY *Anas querquedula (p)*
F   M Skinflats 21 May (AB GO RS).

SHOVELER *Anas clypeata (p)*
F   11 Skinflats 9 Sep (AB). 1 Grangemouth 1 Aug to 22 Oct (DMB MVB
     DT). 4 Kinneil 23 July and 6 from 20 Aug to 28 Oct (BDA DT). 2 L.Ellrig
     14 Dec (TDS).
C   Pair Cambus Pool 25 Mar & 2 on 13 Aug (WRB CJH). 2 Gartmorn 10
     Oct (MC).

POCHARD *Aythya ferina (W)*
F   27 L.Ellrig 12 Feb (TDS). A few Kinneil, with a M on 21 May (DT). 30 -
    > W off Blackness 7 Oct (CJH) & 29 ->NW off Grangemouth on 22nd
    (MVB). 149 Little Denny Res 9 Oct - highest regional WEBS
    count,usual average 3 ! (NB).
C   30 Tullibody Inch 27 Jan (CJH). 79 Gartmorn 15 Oct (MC).
S   70 Carron Valley Res 4 Jan (TDS); 40 on 30 Nov & 23 Dec (AKM JKP).
    39 L.Laggan 22 Jan & 35 L.Coulter on 31st; 21 N.Third Res 28 Feb. 63
    Buckieburn Res 13 Dec - highest previous, 6 (NB).
SWP 83 L.Ard 24 Jan & 59 on 22 Nov; 26 L.Lubnaig 14 Feb, 21 L.Venachar
    & 38 L.Katrine on 15 Dec; other counts less than 20 (NB).

TUFTED DUCK *Aythya fuligula (B,W)*
F   22 Callendar Park 4 Mar (AA). Pair Kinneil 1 May (GO DT). 59 Little
    Denny Res & 60 Black Loch on 9 Oct (NB). 15 Grangemouth 28 Dec
    (GO).
C   184 Gartmorn 12 Nov, 1 pair raised 4Y (MC). 3 AoT on Devon WBS. 2
    Kennetpans 10 Sep (CJH).
S   49 Airthrey 17 Feb; only 1 brood in summer (MVB). F + 3Y Carron
    Valley Res 10 Jul; 144 on 7 Aug & 240 on 7 Oct (AKM). 28 L.Coulter 4
    Sep (NB). 65 N.Third Res 27 Oct (CJH).
SWP 2 pair Ashfield, one with 4Y, Jun (WRB). 3 Pair Cambusmore GP 23
    Jun. 31 L.Watston 18 Mar (CJH). 38 Coustry Lochs 27 Jan, 124 on 8
    Sep. 60 Lake of Menteith 26 Nov & 20 L.Ard 14 Dec, both highest
    WEBS counts (NB).

*SCAUP *Aythya marila (w)*
F   1 L.Ellrig 18 Jan (TDS). 3 Kinneil 28 Oct (BDA); 1 Skinflats 25 Nov
    (GO). 1 Kinneil 23 Jul resembled M Scaup in plumage but bill
    suggested hybrid with Tufted Duck (DT).
S   M in moult Carron Valley Res1 & 10 Jul (AKM). F Airthrey 12 Oct
    (MVB).

EIDER *Somateria mollissima (w)*
F   M Skinflats 15 Jan & 23 May, 2M on 3 Mar; 2M on 7 Dec. 7 (4M)
      Kinneil 8 Apr, 4 (2M) on 15th & 3 on 18th (AB BDA MVB KD GO).
1994: 2 dead, unoiled, Blackness -Dunmore in Feb-Mar (PRG).

GOLDENEYE *Bucephula clangula (W)*
125 Forth Estuary 15 Jan & 42 on 9 Dec (DMB)
F   70 Airth shore 6 Jan (CJH). 12 Carronshore 6 Mar (AB).10 Kinneil 26
    Mar (DT). 26 Black Loch 4 Mar (NB), 6 L.Ellrig 14 Feb (TDS). 1 on Avon
    at Polmont 26 Dec (JW).
C   70 Gartmorn 12 Nov (MC). 11 Kennetpans 3 Dec. 4 on Devon 8 Feb &
    2 on 8 Apr. 11 Cambus 7 Apr (CJH).
S   14 Carron Valley Res in Dec (NB). 23 Cambuskenneth 12 Jan, 55
    Craigforth 30 Dec (CJH MVB).
SWP 20 Blackdub floods 6 Feb,16 L.Dochart 14 Feb, 33 L.Iubhair 14 Mar, 22
    L.Ard,24 L.Venachar & 52 Lake of Menteith on 21st (NB). Last records

1 on Teith 15 Apr & 2F L.Chon on 18th (CJH WRB). lst of autumn F
Coustry Lochs 8 Sept, 40 Lake of Menteith 26 Nov, 15 L.Dochart 21
Nov (NB PWS). 20 Killin 21 Nov & 30 on 8 Dec (PWS).

*SMEW *Mergus albellus (w)*
C   F Gartmorn 17 Dec (PMA).
SWP   F L.Dochart 14 Feb (NB).

RED-BREASTED MERGANSER *Mergus serrator (B,W)*
59 Forth Estuary 15 Jan (DMB).
F   35 Airth Shore 15 Jan (CJH), 43 Skinflats 9 Dec (MVB). 1 Kinneil 22 Sep
       & 11 on 11 Dec (GO AB).
S   3 Carron Valley Res 4 Dec (TDS).
SWP   Pair on Forth at Arnprior 16 Mar & M Coustry Lochs on 24th (DAC
       NB). 2M Lecropt 15 Apr (CJH). 2 Pairs Barbush in April (WRB). Pair on
       Allan Water 22 May to 1 June, 2 juv on 4 Jul (BH). 3 L.Arklet 15 Apr to
       23 May (WRB).
1994: 2 dead, unoiled, Blackness -Dunmore in Feb-Mar (PRG).

GOOSANDER *Mergus merganser (B,W)*
F   3 W.Grangemouth 17 Sep & 14 Carronshore on 29th, 8 on 9 & 28 Dec
       (CJH AB MVB GO). 9 L.Ellrig 8 Jan & 16 on 25 Feb (TDS). 10 Little
       Denny Res 10 Jan; 10 Black Loch 31 Jan & 28 Feb, 10 on 13 Dec (NB).
C   Forth, Tullibody Inch-Cambus: 12 on 3 Jan & 2 Feb (CJH), 34 on 12 Apr
       (WB) & an unprecedented 60 on 14th (DMB).
S   5 L.Laggan 6 Feb; 5 N.Third Res 28 Feb & 6 on 13 Dec (NB). Carron V
       Res: Pair on 25 Mar, 6 on 8 Oct (BDA TDS). 1 ->W Airthrey 15 Aug
       (DMB).
SWP   In spring/summer noted at Craigforth, Doune Ponds, Allan Water,
       L.Mahaick (brood), L.Lubnaig, L.Arklet, L.Chon, Glengyle (brood),
       Glen Lochay (BDA NB WRB BH PWS). 48F L.Ard 26 Sep; 44F Gart
       Loch 18 Oct - roosting, all flew off at dawn (NB).

*RUDDY DUCK *Oxyura jamaicensis (b)*
C   1 Gartmorn 2 Jan, 2M displaying May-June, 2 on 15 Oct & 12 Nov (WB
       MC).
SWP   2M Doune Ponds in Apr but 3(2F) on 22nd, 3 F L.Watson in Sep (WRB
       AD), 5 (2M displaying) Flanders Moss 25 May (TJ).

RED KITE *Milvus milvus*
1991: 1 Braes of Doune 10 Oct, mobbed by crows (CJH). *lst documented
       modern record for area, the editor admits embarrassment in having
       overlooked his own observation.*

*MARSH HARRIER *Circus aeruginosus*
F   1 Skinflats 2 & 13 May "mobbed by everything" (AB GO RS). 1 Kinneil
       18 Aug (BDA).
SWP   1 Glen Dubh (west L.Ard Forest) 23 May (WRB DOE MT)
       *Most of these birds were considerd to be 1st summer females, but it must be
       noted that at this stage some immature males may be indistinguishable (Ed)*

HEN HARRIER *Circus cyaneus (b?, w)*
No definite evidence of nesting; two coastal records. 13 adult males and 13 Ringtails noted (Ed).
F   Slamannan area: singles on 6 Jan, 4 & 25 Feb, 30 Sep, 26 Oct, 17 Dec (AMcI GO TDS). 1 Kinneil 29 Jan & 1 Skinflats 26 Dec (DT GO).
S   1 Blairlogie 16 Jan (BRT). 1 Earlshill 6 Oct (AB). 1 Carron Valley Res 7 Oct (2 on 15th) to 26 Nov (NB AKM GO TDS DT).
1994: M Menstrie 16 Jan (BRT).
SWP 1 L.Macanrie 22 Jan (DT). 3 Flanders Moss 20 Jan, 2 on 17 Feb; 1 on 15 Oct & 1 on 17 Nov (DAC DOE). Thornhill area: 1 on 16 & 19 Apr, 13 Sep, 8 Oct, 23 Dec (NB DAC SS) - hedge hopping seen in (failed) pursuit of small bird. Singles at L.Watston 12 Nov, Ashfield in Oct, Blairdrummond carse 28 Dec (WRB MVB CJH).

*GOSHAWK *Accipiter gentilis*
F   1 Kinneil 23 Dec (CJH).

SPARROWHAWK *Accipiter nisus (B,W)*
F   At Skinflats through year (AB). At Kinneil Jan, Aug to Nov, chased waders and chased by crows (CJH GO). Regular Dunmore when finches on fields (GB). 7 records Slamannan in Jan (AMcI TDS).
C   Bred Woodhill, Birkhill, Vicars Bridge (MC).
S   In Apr & Oct at Plean CP (HMR), Blairlogie May (DAC), Muir Park Mar & Dec (NB). At Stirling garden, F killed by hitting a window 18 Apr (D&RJ).
SWP Through year Ashfield, Dunblane - F killed feral Pigeons in Nov (WRB BH); however, only 1 record (May) in 87 hours observation on CBC block 2 km to west (NB). In spring/summer at Glengyle, L.Ard Forest, Glen Finglas, Arnprior (WRB DAC CJH). In winter/autumn at most of these localities, plus Carse of Stirling.

BUZZARD *Buteo buteo (B,W)*
As breeding bird: widespread SWP, scarce C, increasing S, no proof F.
F   1 at three sites near Slamannan Jan-Feb. 1 Banknock31 Jan & 13 Dec (NB). 1 Castlecary 2 Feb (TDS). 1 Letham Moss 6 Mar (AB), 2 Dunmore Wood Apr-Sep, did not nest (GB). 1Wallacebank 17 Oct (AMcI). 1 Kinnneil 20 Sep (CJH).
C   2 Gartmorn 2 Jan (WB), raised 2Y (MC). Pair bred Muckhart, 2 Pairs Wood Hill (WRB) - 2 Sheardale 28 Mar & 3 Tillicoultry 25 Jul prob same birds (CJH).
S   1 Carron Valley Res 18-29 Jan & 29 Sep 2 on 18 Mar (TDS GO). 2 Stronend 28 Oct, 1 Wardwood 22 Mar (CJH). 4 Kippen 23 Apr, 4 Buchlyvie 12 Nov (DAC). 1 Gargunnock 13 Mar. 3 Pirnhall 8 Aug (BDA), max 3 Plean CP Feb to Oct (HMR) 1 Torwood 29 Jan & 18 Mar (AB DMB). 1 Mine Wood 3 Apr (CJH), 2 Hermitage Wood 12 May & 9 Airthrey 15 Aug (DMB). 2 Cambusbarron 14 Aug (RJ).
SWP In spring/summer: L.Ard Forest - 8 sites (CJH), L.Lubnaig, Blairdrummond Moss, Dunblane, Keir, Cambusmore, 2 pairs

adjoining Doune CBC (DT BH WRB NB). 10 Keir 14 Jan & 12 on 7 Oct (DT), 3 Lake of Menteith18 Feb & 3 L.Watston 9 Sep; 1 on carse Arnieve 20 Dec (CJH).

GOLDEN EAGLE *Aquila chrysaetos (b,w)*
SWP   6 territories checked, probably 6 pairs; 1successful pair reared 2Y (PSA). 1 L.Katrine 19 Nov, 15 Dec (DAC NB).

OSPREY *Pandion haliaetus (p)*
C   1 Gartmorn 28 Aug & lst Sep (MC). 1 ->N Alva 29 Aug (WRB).
S   1 ->E Kippen 1 Aug (MT). 1 Carron V Res 4 Jun to 3 Sep (AKM JM).
SWP 1st seen Trossachs 7 Apr (DT).

KESTREL *Falco tinnunculus (B,W)*
Seen in 41% of 10 Km squares in area during year, but only 2 records in 87 hours on Doune farm CBC (NB).
F   Pair reared 3Y Dunmore (GB). Around Slamannan Jan-Mar (TDS).
C   2 Pairs reared 5Y Wood Hill (MC).
S   4 Carron Valley 8 Oct (TDS). Nest with c/5 L.Arklet 23 May (WRB).
SWP   3 Kinlochard 19 Nov (CJH).

*MERLIN *Falco columbarius (b?,w)*
F   Skinflats-Kinneil: 1 on 2 & 29 Jan; 27 Aug to 23 Dec (AB DMB DT). 1 Strathavon 27 Jan, Slamannan 18 Jan & 24 Nov (TDS).
C   1 Tillicoultry 17 Dec (DMB).
1994: 1 Menstrie 24 Dec (BRT).
S   1 Cringate Law 25 Mar (BDA).
SWP   Singles Lecropt 5 Mar, L.Mahaick 25 Apr, Flanders Moss Nov, Drip carse 7 Dec - chased prey which escaped by flying under van (MVB DOE TJ IW).

PEREGRINE *Falco peregrinus (B,W)*
F   1 territory checked, 1 pair reared 1Y (PSA). Coastal records Jan-Feb & Aug-Sep (GO CJH DT). 1 Fallin 29 Jan (DT). 1 Slamannan 14 Jan - 9 Feb (AMcI TDS).
C   2 territories checked, 2 pairs were successful rearing 4Y (PSA).1 roosted on pylon at Alloa 23 Sep (WRB).
S   6 territories checked, 4 pairs, 3 successful pairs reared 6Y (PSA).
SWP   13 territories checked, 8 pairs & 2 single birds; 5 successful pairs reared 12Y (PSA). Lowland records Jan-May (DMB CJH).

RED GROUSE *Lagopus lagopus (B,W)*
Generally under-recorded
F   Noted Grangeneuk Muir 27 Jan & East Fannyside 14 Oct (TDS).
S   6 (displaying) Kippen Muir 9 Apr (DAC). 2 Earlshill 31 Mar, 20 on 6 Oct (BDA AB). 7 Touch Res 20 Nov (IW). 8 calling by Lossburn path (Sheriffmuir) 21 Oct (NB).
SWP   Calling east L.Arklet 6 May, Pair + 5Y L.Tinker 20 Jun (WRB). 4 in 6.5 km heather Creag Innich 17 Dec (CJH).

PTARMIGAN *Lagopus mutus (b,w)*
No records received

BLACK GROUSE *Tetrao tetrix (B,W)*
There are clearly leks that are not being visited.
S   3 (2M displaying) Cringate Law 7 Jun (GO). 2M at lek West Carron valley Forest 12 Sep &7 Oct (AKM).
SWP   12M Braeleny 29 May & 10M on 28 Dec (DOE CJH). 11 Braes of Doune (Waterside) 25 Apr. Lek heard Braes of Balquhidder 22 Apr (DOE). 6 Ben Ledi 30 Sep (G Murray). M Glen Casaig 10 Dec (CJH). 2 Achray Forest 30 Oct (P Hearn). 2M Ben A'An 30 Apr (SS). 3M, lek, east L.Arklet 26 Apr (WRB).

*CAPERCAILLIE *Tetrao urogallus (b,w)*
SWP   M Drumore Wood 24 May, also M & F found predated at nearby lek (DOE).

GREY PARTRIDGE *Perdix perdix (B,W)*
F   Bred Jupiter WG (C.Ferguson). Pair with chicks E.Grangemouth 10 Aug (DT). 16 Skinflats 14 Jan & 14 on 14 Feb; 7 on 4 Nov & 23 Dec (CJH GO). 6 Airth on 17 Oct & 10 on 3 Dec (IW CJH). 2 pairs bred Drumore (N.Doll), 12 on 3 Nov (GB). 6 California 17 Oct (AMcI). Pair Slamannan (Rigghead) 25 Feb & 9 on 14 Dec (TDS).
S   Pair+ 9Y crossed Plean motorway on 31 Jul (BDA).
SWP   5 Flanders Moss 17 Nov (DOE). 12 Drip carse 9 Dec DAC). 13 Lecropt 9 Dec (MVB). 1pair (seen twice in 87 hours) on Doune CBC (NB).

*QUAIL *Coturnix coturnix*
F   1 Denny (Kirkland) July (C Perkins).
SWP   Thornhill: 1 calling E.Mossside10 Jul & 2 Aug (SS); 2 Brae of Boquhapple 1-6 Aug (G Murray).

PHEASANT *Phasianus colchicus (B,W)*
Abundant (usually by releases) on fields next to keepered estates.
F   1 Skinflats, chocolate brown feathers edged white (GO).
SWP   9.6 AoT per km sq on Doune CBC (NB). 88 (65M) Lecropt 11 Jan (AD).

*WATER RAIL *Rallus aquaticus (w)*
F   1 Skinflats 25 Jan, 1 on 5 Sep (fed with Moorhens) & 2 on 24th (AD GO DMB).
C   1 Gartmorn 8 to 28 Jan (MC).
SWP   1 Thornhill (L.Dhu) 15 Apr (DT).

*CORNCRAKE *Crex crex*
C   1 Alva 14 Sep (MC).
SWP   1 calling Lecropt spring & summer (per DOE).

MOORHEN *Gallinula chloropus (B,W)*
F   5 Kinneil 10 Feb, 18 on 8 Apr & 8 in Sep (AB DT BDA). 5 Skinflats 11 May (BDA). Pair + 6Y Dunmore Wood pond in Jun (GB).

C   2 AoT Cambus in Apr, 2 AoT on Devon WBS (CJH). 6 Delph Pond 18 Dec (BRT).

S   Airthrey: 34 on 17 Feb & 28 on 12 Oct; of 10 pairs only 3 successful, reared 5Y (MVB).

SWP   Pair + juv Ashfield 4 Jul (BH). Pair bred Torrie Lochan (BWB). 8 Blackdub floods 6 Feb & 5 on 24 Nov. 14 Blairdrummond Safari Park pond 23 Feb & 6 on 8 Sep (NB).

COOT *Fulica atra (B,W)*

F   Pair (+4 juv in Jul) Kinneil (GO DT). Pair + 2 Juv Skinflats May-Jun (BDA AB GO). 2 pair + 5Y Callendar Park 11 Jun (BDA). 20 Little Denny Res 10 Jan - typical new year influx (NB).

C   12 Cambus 4 Mar, 3 AoT in Apr (BDA CJH). 1 AoT on Devon WBS (CJH). 547 Gartmorn in Nov (NB).

S   Airthrey: 50 on 17 Feb & 32 on 15 Dec; 14 prs with only 4Y fledged from 5 prs (MVB).

SWP   80 Lake of Menteith 22 Jan, 167 on Oct 15 & 109 on 19 Dec (NB). 17 L.Watston 18 Mar & 18 on 15 Oct (CJH). 29 Coustry Ponds 23 Mar & 51 on 8 Sep. 50 Gart 17 Jan & 107 on 22 Dec (NB). Pair bred Torrie Lochan (BWB).

OYSTERCATCHER *Haematopus ostralegus (B,W)*

F   3 L.Ellrig 25 Feb (TDS). 60 Airth shore 12 Feb (CJH). Kinneil: 70 on 23 Jul, 120 on 18 Nov, partial albino present through year (AB DT CJH). Skinflats: 55 on 19 Jul, 26 on 10 Sep; pair hatched 2 Y (AB MVB GO). Bred N.Doll (Dunmore) (GB).

C   1 Airthrey 10 Feb, carrying worms to University roof 12 May (MVB CJH). 5 AoT Devon WBS (CJH). 39 Gartmorn 2 Mar (WB).

S   40 Craigforth 5 Feb, 160 on 12th, 430 on 18th & 480 on 2 Mar (DT MVB CJH). Pair bred Carron Valley Res (AKM).

SWP   180 Blackdub 8 Feb (NB)- *c1 km from Craigforth, Ed.* 11 L.Watston 14 Feb & 48 on 18 Mar (CJH). 274 Gart 13 Mar & 373 Coustry on 23rd (NB). 12 AoT per sq Km on Doune CBC (NB); 5 AoT L.Mahaick 25 Apr (DOE); 3 AoT Cambusmore GP 14 May (CJH). 20 Dunblane 20 Jun (BH).

RINGED PLOVER *Charadrius hiaticula (b,W)*

F   9 Skinflats 14 Jan, 16 on 16 May, 5 on 14 Jul (MVB GO BDA). 11 Grangemouth 26 Feb, 72 on 27 Aug (DMB GB). 15 Kinneil 2 Jan, 15 on 18 Aug (DT BDA). 1 N.Doll (Dunmore) 20 May (GB).

C   1 Gartmorn 2 Mar (WB).

S   Pair bred Carron V Res, 5 on 29 Jul (AKM). 1 AoT Lower Earlsburn Res 12 Jun (BDA).

SWP   Pair +1Y Barbush GP Jul (WRB).

GOLDEN PLOVER *Pluvialis apricaria (B,W)*
The small number of likely breeding records may indicate a reduction in range compared with twenty years ago. Passage in spring (inland) and

October (especially by estuary) is well demonstrated (Ed).
206 Forth Estuary 15 Jan & 809 on 22 Oct (DMB).
F   Skinflats: 1 on 11 Aug, 91 on 10 Sep, 200 on 2 Oct, 800 on 9 Nov & 85
     on 9 Dec (GO MVB AB DMB). Kinneil: 30 on 29 Jan; 5 on 9 Aug & 204
     on 13 Dec (CJH DT). Noted near Slamannan 7 Feb & 6 Mar (TDS). 200
     Stenhousemuir 19 Apr (GB).
C   3 Ben Buck 6 Aug (WRB).
SWP Carse of Stirling:115 Blairdrummond on 4 Mar, 400 Drip on 18th & 100
     on 20th, 50 Arnieve 14 Dec (DT IW DAC RJ CJH).

GREY PLOVER *Pluvialis squatarola (W)*
75 Forth estuary 22 Oct (DMB)
F   Skinflats: 25 on 14 Jan; 3 on 11 Aug, 14 on 14 Sep, 73 on 22 Oct & 6 on
     6 Nov (CJH GO DMB AB MVB). 10 flew in high from east at
     Grangemouth on 10 Sep (DT). Few at Kinneil, lst of autumn 1 on 12
     Aug (GO).
C   3 Tullibody Inch 20 Sep (WRB).

LAPWING *Vanellus vanellus (B,W)*
2926 Forth Estuary 9 Dec (DMB).
F   Skinflats: 490 on 15 Jan, 160 on 13 Aug, 860 on 10 Sep, 560 on 9 Dec
     (MVB). Kinneil: 520 on 4 Feb; 150 on 16 Jul, 300 on 3 Sep & 1000 on
     16th,1360 on 13 Dec (CJH DT AB DMB). On territory Slamannan 15
     Feb (TDS). 6 AoT N.Doll, chicks in mid May, left in early June (GB).
C   Kennetpans: 380 on 22 Oct &360 on 23 Dec (CJH). Tullibody Inch: 350
     on 20 Aug, 2200 on 14 Sep & 2500 on 20th (CJH DMB WRB). 2 AoT
     Cambus Apr-May. 18 AoT Devon WBS (CJH).
S   30 AoT Bandeath 13 May (DMB). 366 Taylorton 23 Dec (NB).
SWP Frequent display Kippenrait on 12 Mar & Gargunnock carse on 13th
     (CJH). 200 Cambusmore 20 Aug (PWS). Lecropt: 70 on 24 Feb, 600 on
     5 Mar; 500 on 28 Aug & 9 Sep, 200 on 10 Oct (AD MVB NB WRB). 4
     AoT on Doune CBC (NB). 20 AoT L.Mahaick 25 Apr (DOE). 2 AoT
     L.Arklet 6 May (WRB).

KNOT *Calidris canutus (W)*
1202 Forth Estuary 15 Jan & 1391 on 9 Dec (DMB).
F   Kinneil: 2700 on 8 Jan, 170 on 18 Mar; 3 on 29 Jul, 10 on 1 Aug, 80 on
     24 Sep, 1500 on 18 Nov, 2500 on 2 Dec & 3000 on 11th & 16th (AB CJH
     DT DMB). Skinflats: lst on 14 Jul, 20 on 27 Aug (GO DMB).

*SANDERLING *Calidris alba (p)*
F   1 Skinflats 2 May & 13 Aug (AB GO DMB). 1 Kinneil 29 Jul (AB). 2
     Grangemouth 10 Sep (DT).

*LITTLE STINT *Calidris minuta (p)*
F   Skinflats: 1 on 13 Sep, 1 on 6 & 7 Oct (GO AB).

CURLEW SANDPIPER *Calidris ferruginea (p)*
17 Forth Estuary 9 Sep (DMB).

F   Skinflats:1 on 1 May; 1 on 27 Aug, 15 on 11 Sep & 5 on 17th & 25th, 1
      on 7 Oct (GO DMB RS WRB AB). 2 Grangemouth 27 Aug & 12 on 10
      Sep (DMB DT). Kinneil: 8 on 10 Sep,10 on 16th & 2 on 21st(DMB GO).
      Area Summary (half monthly)

Aug	Sep	Oct
0 3	35 15	1 0

DUNLIN *Calidris alpina* (b?,W)
5144 Forth Estuary 12 Feb & 10975 on 9 Dec (DMB).

F   Kinneil: 650 on 26 Feb, 2000 on 18 Mar, 1100 on 1 Apr, 220 on 1 May;
      9 on 17 Jul, 86 on 18 Aug, 400 on 3 Dec (DT CJH BDA). Skinflats: 3450
      on 15 Jan, 800 on 12 Feb, 50 on 2 May; 25 on 28 Jul,180 on 29 Aug, 700
      on 10 Sep, 900 on 22 Oct, 4880 on 9 Dec (MVB CJH AB BDA).

S   7 Carron V Res 3 Jul (DMB) - presumably early migrants (Ed)..

RUFF *Philomachus pugnax* (p)
F   Skinflats: 3 on 7 Sep & 4 on 8th, last 1 on 14th (GO AB). Kinneil: 1 on
      13 May; 1 on 12 Aug, 7 on 13 Sep & 6 on 16th, 1 on 5 Nov (GO IW CJH
      DMB).

C   1 Cambus 20 Aug (PMA). 2 Tullibody Inch 23 Aug & 6 on 26th, 4 on
      14 Sept & 7 on 20th (MVB DMB WRB).
      Area Summary (half monthly)

Aug	Sep	Oct	Nov
1 7	15 13	0 0	1 0

JACK SNIPE *Lymnocryptes minimus* (w)
F   Kinneil: 9 on 1 Jan, 2 on 7th & 1 on 29th, 1 on 7 Mar; 7 on 5 Nov, 3 on
      12 Dec & 1 on 26th (GO RS DT). 4 E.Grangemouth 9 Dec (DMB). 3
      Skinflats 7 Jan (AB). 1 Kincardine Bridge 23 Dec (CJH). 1 Lathallan 26
      Dec (JW). 1 Slamannan 24 Dec (TDS).
SWP   1 Flanders Moss 12 Dec (TJ).

SNIPE *Gallinago gallinago (B,W)*
Probably under-recorded in breeding season but may have decreased (Ed).
F   Kinneil: 15 on 1 Jan; 7 on 1 Aug & 25 on 20th, 34 on 16 Sep, 10 on 5
      Nov (RS DT GO). 11 Grangemouth 20 Aug, 14 on 10 Sep, 22 on 9
      Dec(DT DMB). 14 Skinflats 12 Nov, 5 on 9 Dec (AB GO). On territory
      Slamannan 15 Feb (TDS).
C   1 AoT Devon WBS. 15 Diverswell 8 Apr & 3 on 6 Jul (CJH). 4 Cambus
      13 Aug & 10 on 1 Sep (CJH IW).
SWP   Max 3 Ashfield 19 Dec (WRB). 10 Forth-Allan 1 Jan &12 on 12 Sep (DT
      CJH). 1 Aot Glen Buckie 30 Apr & 8 L.Mahaick on 25th, 2 AoT
      L.Arklet; 2 L.Tinker 20 Jun (DT DOE WRB). 7 Flanders Moss 15 Oct
      (DAC). 7 Pendreich 24 Dec (CJH).

WOODCOCK *Scolopax rusticola (B,W)*
Under-recorded in breeding season (Ed).
F   3 Slamannan 24 Jan (TDS). 1 Dunmore 6 May & 27 Aug (DT GB). 1
      Skinflats 18 Nov (GO). 1 Polmont 26 Dec (JW).
S   1 Torwood 1 Apr & 4 on 23rd (SS AB). 1 Touch Res 14 Feb (IW).

SWP   In spring/summer at Rhuveag, Brig o'Turk, Lake of Menteith, (SS DT). Singles L.Macanrie Jan-Feb, & in Dec at Flanders Moss, Thornhill, Dunblane (DT DOE SS IW WRB NB).

BLACK-TAILED GODWIT *Limosa limosa (W)*
F   Moderate numbers were at Kinneil from January to mid-May and from July to the year end with a max of 68 on 24 September. Skinflats was only used erratically; the apparent rise in the area total in early April is probably double counting of the same birds whilst the low count late November is probably lack of observation. A bird at Skinflats on 15 July had an orange ring, placed above leg joint (AB BDA DMB CJH GO RS DT).
C   2 Tullibody Inch 26 Aug & 3 on 20 Sep (DMB WRB).

	Jan	Feb	Mar	Apr	May	Jun	Jul	Aug	Sep	Oct	Nov	Dec
Knnl	26 19	13 26	20 22	25 23	19 1	0 0	3 22	18 42	43 68	31 21	1 43	28 42
Sknf	0 1	0 0	0 0	12 0	1 2	0 0	16 4	0 4	8 15	0 0	0 0	0 0
Area	26 20	13 26	20 22	37 23	20 3	0 0	19 26	18 48	51 86	31 21	1 43	28 42

BAR-TAILED GODWIT *Limosa lapponica (W)*
220 Forth Estuary 15 Jan & 281 on 9 Dec (DMB).
F   Kinneil: 200 on 29 Jan,141 on 4 Feb & 120 on 26th, 110 on 8 Mar, a few on 18 Apr; lst of autumn 1 on 16 Jul, 6 on 12 Aug, 105 on 18 Nov, 250 on 11 & 16 Dec (AB CJH DT). Skinflats: 3 on 16 May & 2 on 19th; 1 on 3 Jul & 8 on 12th, 6 on 28 Aug & 22 Oct (BDA GO MVB). On 25 Sep, 25 flew W (inland) at Skinflats (AB).

WHIMBREL *Numenius phaeopus (p)*
F   Skinflats: 7 on 11 May, left N; 1st of autumn 9 on 12 Jul, 3 on 18 Aug (flew E) & 3 on 27th, last on 10 Sep. Kinneil: 1 on 4 & 13 May; 1st of autumn on 15 Jul, 4 on 9 Aug, last on 9 Sep (AB DMB GO RS DT). 3 Grangemouth 12 Aug & 1 on 12 Sep (DT).
SWP   1 L.Arklet 30 Apr (WRB).
   Area Summary (half monthly)

May	Jun	Jul	Aug	Sep
8 0	0 0	10 4	6 3	4 0

CURLEW *Numenius arquata (B,W)*
The March return & passage is clear in inland records (Ed).
985 Forth Estuary 15 Jan & 1349 on 10 Sept (DMB).
F   Kinneil: 160 on 26 Feb; 120 on 9 Jul & 300 on 16th, 531 on 13 Aug, 780 on 10 Sep (DT DMB). Skinflats: 300 on 16 Jan, 168 on 10 Feb, 27 on 31 Mar; 15 on 3 Jul, 209 on 13 Aug, 560 on 22 Oct, 220 on 9 Dec (AB MVB). Inland return: 1 L.Ellrig 8 Jan & 5 on 28 Feb; 3 Slamannan 6 Mar (TDS NB). Pair N.Doll in June (GB).
C   90 Tullibody Inch 27Jan, 100 Kennetpans 13 Dec (CJH). 42 Tillicoultry 10 Mar (BRT). 3 AoT Devon WBS.
S   100 (roost) Kippen Muir 27 Mar (DAC).
SWP   40 Lecropt, 33 Gart & 22 L.Voil 14 Mar (DT NB). 30 AoT L.Mahaick 25 Apr (DOE). Pair at Carron Valley Res & two on Doune CBS (AKM

NB). 3 ->SW Dunblane 26 Jun, heard over BoA on p.m of 27th - probably departure from breeding sites (MVB CJH).

SPOTTED REDSHANK *Tringa erythropus (p)*
F   Skinflats: 1 27 Feb to 29 Apr; 1 in BP 12 Jul, 2 on 10 Sep & 1 to 13th. 1 E.Grangemouth 27 Aug. 1 Kinneil 19 Aug,1 9 & 24 Sep. (BDA AB DMB AD CJH GO RS DT).

REDSHANK *Tringa totanus (B,W)*
2370 Forth Estuary 15 Jan & 3177 on 9 Dec (DMB).
F   Skinflats: 1000 on 15 Jan, 420 on 12 Feb; 250 on 28 Jul, 337 on 13 Aug, 810 on 10 Sep, 1100 on 22 Oct, 810 on 9 Dec. (AB MVB CJH). 350 Grangemouth 20 Aug. Kinneil: 450 on 8 Apr & 820 on 16th; 280 on 16 Jul & 400 on 28th (DT). 114 Higgins Neuk 15 Jan. 250 Blackness 7 Oct (CJH).
C   50 Tullibody Inch 27 Jan. 4 AoT Devon CBS (CJH).
S   1 Kippen Muir 27 Mar & 6 on 2 Apr (DAC). Pair bred Carron Valley Res (AKM).
SWP 1 Lake of Menteith 19 Dec (NB) - *mid-winter records inland unusual, Ed.* 2 Lecropt 19 Mar (DT). 2 Pairs Ashfield (WRB). 7 AoT L.Mahaick 25 Apr (DOE).

GREENSHANK *Tringa nebularia (p)*
F   Skinflats: 1 on 14 Jul, 1 on 10 to 13 Aug, 1 on 12 Sep to 28 Oct with 3 on 17 Sep & 2 on 20 Oct. 1 Grangemouth 17 Sep. Kinneil: 1 on 9 & 11 Jul, 1 or 2 from 5 Aug to 20 Sep with 3 on 15 Sep, last on 21 Oct (BDA AB DMB WRB GO RS IW).
C   1 Cambus 22 Apr (CJH). 2 Tullibody Inch 26 Aug & 1 on 31st (DMB CJH).
S   2 Carron Valley Res 5 Sep, 1 on 12th & 14th (AKM RKP).
     Area Summary (half monthly)

Apr	May	Jun	Jul	Aug	Sep	Oct
0 1	0 0	0 0	2 0	3 4	6 4	1 3

*GREEN SANDPIPER *Tringa ochropus (p)*
F   1 on R.Carron at Larbert 18 Jul (GO J.Marshall). 1 Skinflats 25 Jul & 2 on 30th (AB DT).

*WOOD SANDPIPER *Tringa glareola*
F   1 imm Skinflats 12 Sep, harassed by plovers (GO).

COMMON SANDPIPER *Tringa hypoleucos (B)*
F   Kinneil: lst on 11 Jul, 9 on 16th & 11 on 23rd, 6 on 5 Aug , last on 27th. 1 at Skinflats 25 Apr. 4 Grangemouth 17 Aug. (BDA AB DMB GO DT). 1 AoT on Avon at Grangemouth 25 Jun (RS).
C   1 Dollar 10 Apr (WRB). 1 Cambus 22 Apr. 3 AoT on Devon WBS (CJH). 2 Tullibody Inch 30 Jul & 4 on 26 Aug (CJH DMB).
S   1 Touch Res 16 Apr (IW). 7 Carron Valley Res 29 Jul & 2 on 18 Aug (AKM).
SWP 1 Lecropt 15 Apr (CJH). 1 Dunblane 1 May, 2 AoT on 14th, last on 4 Jul

(BH). In summer at Barbush-Kinbuck (3 AoT), Doune CBC (2 AoT), Glengyle-Stronachlachar (5 AoT), L.Arklet (3 AoT). (WRB NB). Last 1 Cambusmore 20 Aug (PWS).
Area autumn totals :

Jul		Aug		Sep	
9	20	6	11	0	0

TURNSTONE *Arenaria interpres (W)*
45 Forth Estuary 15 Jan (DMB).
F   Blackness: 12 on 2 Jan; 16 on 7 Oct & 11 on 18 Nov (DT CJH). 4 Kinneil 23 Jul (DT). 5 Skinflats 15 Mar & 8 on 7 May (DMB AB).

ARCTIC SKUA *Stercorarius parasiticus (p)*
F   2 juv Blackness 7 Oct, chasing Sandwich terns (AB CJH). Grangemouth area: 2 on 9 Aug, regular to 17 Sep with 7 on 10 Sept & 6 on 17th, last 1 on 12 Nov (AB DMB GO DT).

*GREAT SKUA *Stercorarius skua (p)*
F   2 -> W Grangemouth 10 Sept (DT).

*SABINE'S GULL *Xema sabini*
F   1 Grangemouth 26 Aug (DT). *2nd record for area.*
Seen briefly and fairly close in flight, then afloat and making repositioning flights at several hundred metres range, x10 binoculars and x20 telescope. Long wings with upperwing pattern of solid black primaries, greyish, brown-tinged coverts and broad, triangular white trailing area; underwing largely whitish but with dark lateral bar along centre of inner wing. Smaller than a Kittiwake seen just before, round -headed with short, dark bill. Underparts and head mainly white with dark markings behind eye giving a masked effect; hind crown down to hind neck brownish, extending down to side of upper breast and merging on back with greyish mantle. Rump and tail white with black terminal bar, tail sharp cornered but not obviously forked. The bird gave one grating call in flight, afloat it occasionally pecked at debris on the water. *Resume of more detailed notes and sketches, accepted by Stirling Records Panel as an immatureSabine's Gull, probably a 1st summer bird, though the possibility of an early moulting juvenile cannot be entirely excluded (Ed).*

BLACK-HEADED GULL *Larus ridibundus (B,W)*
F   130 Skinflats 3 Jul (AB). 1100 Higgins Neuk & 1500 Airth shore on 10 Sept, hawking (CJH). Thousands at Lathallan in Nov in field spread with sewage sludge (JW).
C   300 hawking Alva 25 Jul, 700 there on 16 Nov following plough. 580 Alloa Inch 22 Nov (CJH).
S   8 nests, 5 with young, Carron Valley Res 30 May (AKM). 300 hawking BoA16 Aug (CJH), 100 hawking craneflies Airthrey 31 Oct (MVB). 1200 Blairlogie 9 Sep, on grassy stubble (CJH).
SWP 120 AoT raised 80Y Ashfield (WRB). 579 birds Cambusmore GP 14

Mar, 270 AoT on 14 May, 330 adults there on 23 Jun (NB CJH). 800
Blairdrummond 6 Feb & 635 Blackdub floods 27 Oct (NB).

1994:   12 dead, unoiled, Blackness -Dunmore in Feb-Mar (PRG).

COMMON GULL *Larus canus (B,W)*

F   378 L.Ellrig 9 Oct (NB).

SWP   40 AoT Cambusmore GP 14 May, 60 adults on 23 Jun (CJH). 2 AoT
L.Arklet, birds at L.Chon probably robbed (WRB). 15 AoT L.Tinker 26
Apr (DOE). 700 roosted L.Venachar 8 Oct (CJH). 400 Gart 10 Oct & 600
on 20 Nov (PWS).

1994:   6 dead, unoiled, Blackness -Dunmore in Feb-Mar (PRG).

LESSER BLACK-BACKED GULL *Larus fuscus (b,S)0*
*Few mid-winter records, as usual; increasing nest attempts on roofs; more stayed late
into autumn.*

F   1 Kinneil 1 Jan (RS). 3 mouth of R.Carron 21 Jan (GO). Spring arrivals:
2 Grangemouth 26 Feb, 7 on 4 Mar; 1 L.Ellrig 6 Mar, 500 flew W in 6hrs
Banknock-Avonside on 23 Mar (GB GO TDS BDA). 3 pairs bred near
Jupiter WG (C Ferguson). Adult with unfledged young on river cairn
at Grangemouth 1 Jul (DMB). 27 Skinflats 28 Jul & 45 on 4 Aug (AB).
67 Little Denny Res 6 Oct (NB).

C   3 around Menstrie bond roofs 30 Apr & 1 very anxious 15 Jul. 2 Alva
16 Nov , 1 Kennetpans 9 Dec (CJH).

S   2 Stirling carse 19 Feb (DT). 60 Buchlyvie 14 Oct (CJH).

SWP   Midwinter: 1 Lecropt 1 Jan & 9 Dec (DT), 2 Killin 8 Dec & 1 on 11th
(PWS). 3 AoT Cambusmore Gp 23 Jun (CJH). 300 Blairdrummond 21
Oct & 70 Thornhill on 25th (DT CJH).

HERRING GULL *Larus argentatus (b?,S,W)*

F   2500 Kinneil 23 Dec (CJH).

S   Roosting Cambus-Tullibody Inch: 6000 on 23 Aug, 2000 on 6 Sept,
2400 on 1 Nov 7, 2700 on the 17th (MVB CJH).

1994:   20 dead, unoiled, Blackness -Dunmore in Feb-Mar (PRG).

*ICELAND GULL *Larus glaucoides*

SWP   1 Quarry Loch, Blairdrummond 27 Jan. With Common and
Blackheaded Gulls, uniform creamy -grey, size about Herring Gull
but head rounded, black tipped bill, probably 2nd winter (NB).

GREAT BLACK-BACKED GULL *Larus marinus (S,W)*
Highly under-reported (Ed).

F   60 Kinneil 17 Sep (CJH). 2 Slamannan 1 Dec (TDS).

C   85 Tullibody Inch 20 Sep (WRB).

1994:   5 dead, unoiled, Blackness -Dunmore in Feb-Mar (PRG).

*KITTIWAKE *Rissa tridactyla (P,w)*

F   1 ->W Grangemouth 26 Aug, 1 on 27th & 3 (2 juv) ->W on 17 Sep
(DT). 1 Blackness 7 Oct (CJH).

1994:   2 dead, unoiled, Blackness -Dunmore in Feb-Mar (PRG).

SANDWICH TERN *Sterna sandvicensis (P)*
F   70 Carriden 13 Aug (DMB). 20 Blackness 13 Sep & 45 on 7 Oct - one
       with white/lilac colour ring (AB CJH).150 Kinneil 30 Aug & 100 on 16
       Sep (DT DMB). 52 Skinflats 13 Sep (GO). 2 flew high W over R.Carron
       on 26 Jul (AB).
C   16 Kennetpans 10 Sep & 12 on 16th. 4 Cambus 20 Sep , last 2 S.Alloa
       on 15 Oct. (CJH WRB DMB).

COMMON TERN *Sterna hirundo (B)*
F   lst, 2 Skinflats 4 May (BDA). 32 Grangemouth 6 May (DT), at the
       colony on 1Jul there were 104 pairs, at least 70Y reared (DMB). 20 ->
       W Kinneil 20 Aug (AB).
C   1 Kennetpans 16 Sep, last record (WRB).
S   1 AoT Carron V Res 30 May (AKM).

*ARCTIC TERN *Sterna paradisaea*
F   1 - a sickly Juv - Blackness 7 Oct (CJH).

*BLACK TERN *Chlidonias niger*
F   2 Grangemouth 13 Aug & 1 on 20th, 2 -> W at Kinneil 20 Aug (DMB
       DT AB).

GUILLEMOT *Uria aalge (W)*
F   1 Skinflats 18 Nov & 2 on 7th to 23rd, 2 Grangemouth 9 Dec, 1 dead
       Kinneil on 17th & 15 Kincardine Bridge on 20th (GO AB MVB DMB
       DT WRB).
C   13 Kennetpans 9 Dec (CJH).
1994: 633 dead (+5 sick), unoiled, Blackness -Dunmore in Feb-Mar. 2 birds
       at Blackness & 1 at Kincardine Bridge were ringed : 1 from Fair Isle
       (19.6.93), 1 from N.Sutor (Nigg, 20.6.86), 1 from Isle of May (20.6.93)
       (PRG).

*RAZORBILL *Alca torda (w)*
F   1 Carriden 9 Dec (DMB).
1994: 10 dead, unoiled, Blackness -Dunmore in Feb-Mar (PRG).

*LITTLE AUK *Alle alle*
F   2 Kinneil 22 Nov (CJH). Birds were found alive and taken to SSPCA:
       2 at Stirling on 29 Nov, 1 at Falkirk on 6 Dec & 8 on 7th; unfortunately
       all soon died (per SSPCA).
SWP   1 L.Chon 15 Dec - picked up and released on L.Lomond (R.Duel).

ROCK DOVE / FERAL PIGEON *Columba livia (B,W)*
F   230 Skinflats 30 Sep, 150 Kinneil 2 Dec (CJH).
C   155 on tilled field Alva 26 May (CJH).
S   180 Blairlogie 16 Jan (BRT).
SWP   100 Dunblane through year (BH).

STOCK DOVE *Columba oenas (B,W)*
F   16 Skinflats 29 Jan, 22 on 12 Jul, 26 on 18 Nov, 45 on 26 Dec (AB GO).

6 Kinneil 15 Apr, 22 on 13 May & 9 on 26 Dec (BDA GO). 4 Slamannan
2 Jan (TDS).
C   5 Diverswell 31 May (CJH).
S   4 Pendreich 9 Nov (CJH).
SWP   5 Kinbuck 10 Dec (WRB).

WOODPIGEON *Columba palumba (B,W)*
F   600 Larbert in Jan (WRB). 400 Kinneil 29 Jan & 886 on 26 Dec (CJH
     GO).   Max Skinflats 54 on 30 May (GO).
C   299 Alva 18 Mar, on grass (NB).
S   Passage W at Airthrey on 1 Nov (MVB).
SWP   700 Lecropt 14 Jan & 800 on 28th (DT MVB). 400 Argaty 16 Aug, in
     rape stubble (NB). 440 L.Watston 12 Nov. 400 -> W, Braes of Doune
     21 Oct & 175 ->N, Kippenrait 1 Nov; however 114 -> S, Pass of Leny
     on 29 Oct - on all these dates there was a series of parties in steady
     flight (CJH). 50 L.Katrine 15 Dec feeding on beech mast (NB).

COLLARED DOVE *Streptopelia decaocto (B,W)*
Under-reported, but scarce away from suburbs and large farms (Ed)
F   3 Skinflats 7 Sep (GO). Max 6 Carronshore 30 Mar (AB). 1 N.Doll
     (Dunmore) 27 Jul -lst record (GB).
S   10 Plean 2 Apr (DT).
SWP   1 pair on Doune CBC (NB). 2 Killin 1 Oct (PWS).

*TURTLE DOVE *Streptopelia turtur*
SWP   1 singing Thornhill 8 May (SS).

CUCKOO *Cuculus canorus (B)*
     1st records at Thornhill on 1 May, L.Venachar on 3rd, Sheriffmuir on
     5th, L.Chon & L.Arklet on 6th, Blairlogie on 8th, Gartmorn on 9th,
     Auchenbowie on 11th (SS IW AD WRB DAC WB BDA).
     Summer records at L.Arklet, L.Ard Forest, Menteith Hills, Bracklinn
     Falls, Dunblane, North Third, Dunmore (BDA WRB DT BH JP GB).
     Last records in August - Menstrie Moss on 1st, Sheriffmuir on 5th &
     Kinneil on 13th (WRB MVB DT).

*BARN OWL *Tyto alba (b,w)*
F   1 found dead Kinneil 4 Mar (GO). 2 around mine shaft at Denny in Jul
     (C.Perkins).
SWP   1 L.Arklet 13 May (A.Fail), 1 Thronhill carse late Jun (WRB),1 Keir 4 Jul
     (DMB).

TAWNY OWL *Strix aluco (B,W)*
F   Slamannan: 2 Crossburn 8 Jan & 1 Bogside 17 Feb (TDS).
C   Pair reared 2Y Gartmorn 26 May (MC). Calling Alva in Sep (PMA).
SWP   In Trossachs nestboxes 18 attempts reared 18Y (HR). Also recorded
     Lecropt, Blackdub, Blairdrummond, Ashfield (IW BDA WRB).

*LONG-EARED OWL *Asio otus (b,w)*
F   1 Slamannan, Bogbridge,7 Jan (TDS). 1 Skinflats 29 Apr (BDA).

SHORT-EARED OWL *Asio flammeus (b,W)*
F   1 Fallin 29 Jan (DT). 1 Shortrig Mire 22 & 25 Feb (TDS). 1 Skinflats 3
       Oct & 2 on 28th, 1 on 28 Dec (AB GO). 1 E.Grangemouth 22 Oct
       (DMB). 1Kinneil 29 Apr & 11 Nov (DAC BDA).
C   1 Cambus 25 Mar & 3 Sep (WRB CJH).
S   1 Earlshill in Jan (WRB). 1 Kippen Muir 27 Mar & 1 L.Coulter on 29th
       (DAC).
SWP   1 Flanders Moss 6 Mar & 4 Apr (DOE TJ). 1 L.Tinker 20 Jun (WRB). 1
       Arivurichardich 22 May & 1 Jul (SS). 1 Arnieve, Gargunnock carse, 12
       - 30 Dec (CJH). 1 Hutchison 17 Dec (WRB).

NIGHTJAR *Caprimulgus europaeus (?b)*
SWP   None found Queen Elizabeth Forest Park this summer (per Forest
       Enterprise).

SWIFT *Apus apus (B)*
       1st records: 2 Stirling & 3 Dunblane on 3 May, 1 Letham & 9 BoA on 4th, 6
       Doune on 5th (DT BH GB CJH BDA). Last records in August: Dunblane &
       BoA on 11th, 10 at Plean on 13th (NB CJH DT).
F   63 Skinflats 1 Jun (GO).
S   Max 60 BoA 25 Jul (CJH).
SWP   Max Dunblane 12 on 26 May & 14 Jul (BH).

*KINGFISHER *Alcedo atthis (b,w)*
F   1 Kinneil 10 Sep & 12 Dec (DMB DT). 1 Grangemouth 25 Jun & 1 on
       Carron at Larbert 6 Aug (RS GO J.Marshall).
C   1 AoT on Devon WBS (CJH), 1 at Kersiepow 20 Nov (NB). 1 Cambus
       4 Mar & 9 Apr, 1 Blackdevonmouth 16 Sep (BDA WB WRB).
S   2 Airthrey 19 Jan, 1 on 17 Feb (MVB). 1 BoA 12 Sep (CJH).
SWP   1 L.Venachar 4 Aug (JS). 1 Gart during summer (per NB). 1 L.Tay,
       Acharn Fishery, 31 Oct (PWS). 1 L.Dochart 28 Nov (NB). 1 Ashfield 1
       Sep & 4 Dec (WRB).

GREEN WOODPECKER *Picus viridis (B,W)*
F   Slamannan: 1 E.Loanrig 25 Jan & 1 Rashiehill 11 Oct (TDS).
C   1 Myretoun 30 Apr, 2 Juv at Menstrie Glen & also noted Wood Hill &
       Muckhart (CJH WRB).
S   2 Plean CP 23 Jan, nested (HMR). 1 N.Third 30 Apr & 30 May (BDA).
       1 Kippen 1 Aug (MT). 1 Sheriffmuir 21 Oct on fence posts (NB).1
       Carron V Res 19 Jan & 12 Oct (TDS).
SWP   3 AoT L.Ard Forest (WRB CJH). 2 L.Dhu 15 Apr & 1 L.Rusky on 24th
       (DT DOE).

GREAT SPOTTED WOODPECKER *Dendrocopus major (B,W)*
Greatly under reported from S & SWP
F   1 Slamannan 6 Mar (TDS). 1 Castlecary 24 Jun & 18 Aug (BDA). Bred
       Dunmore Wood but 2 Juv killed by cat (GB). 1 Skinflats 22 Oct (AB
       MVB). 1 Polmont 29 Dec (JW).
S   At Plean CP 12 Apr - 31 Oct, 3 on 4 Apr, probably bred (HMR DT).

Noted Mine Wood, Blairlogie, Sauchieburn (WRB DAC BDA).
SWP   1 L.Voil 14 Feb (NB). 2 AoT Drumore (WRB CJH). 1 Drip Carse 18 Mar,
F+2J on 20 Jun (IW BDA). 1 on Doune CBC 20 Jun. Bred Kilbryde, 2 Y
close to fledging on 14 Jun (NB). In Nov 1 at Stronachlachar &
Dunblane (DAC R.Bashford).

SKYLARK *Alauda arvensis (B,W)*
F   Singing Slamannan 11 Feb (TDS). 115 in stubble Airth shore 16 Jan
(CJH). 70 Kinneil 29 Jan, small passage SW on 8 Oct (DT). 45 Skinflats
29 Jan; 50 on 6 Oct, 600 on 24 Dec (AB GO).
C   13 AoT on 5 Km of lower Devon (CJH).
SWP   11 AoT per sq Km on Doune CBC - increase from 1994 (NB). 4 AoT
L.Arklet (WRB). 90 Lecropt 14 Jan, 120 on 26 Feb & 220 on 5 Mar; small
passage W on 7 Oct (MVB DT). 160 in stubble Drip Carse 2 Mar (CJH).
100 Thornhill Carse 14 Oct (DAC).

SAND MARTIN *Riparia riparia (B)*
1st records: 3 Carron Valley Res on 2 April, 2 Dunblane, 3 Airthrey & 6 Lake
of Menteith on 3rd, 15 Carronshore on 8th; 50 Dunblane on 9th & 100
Airthrey on 18th (BDA DMB BH DT AB MVB). Last, 20 Dunblane on 7 Sep &
3 Cambus on 10th (BH CJH).
F   70 Kinneil 16 Jul & 50 on 29th (DT AB).
C   6 nests on Devon WBS (CJH).
S   7 nests on Forth W of Gargunnock sawmill 23 Jun (CJH).
SWP   Nest counts: 200 nests Barbush (WRB), 20 Allan Water landslip (BH),
60 Cambusmore GP (CJH).

SWALLOW *Hirundo rustica (B)*
1st records: 1 Carron Valley Res 2 Apr, 1 Falkirk on 8th, 1 Skinflats & 1
Dunblane on 9th, 1 Plean on 12th: widespread from 17th (BDA AB BH AD).
Last 250 Cambus on 20 Sep, 1 Carronshore on 6 Oct , 2 Lecropt & 1 Blackness
on 7th, 3 Falkirk on 16th, & 1 Aberfoyle on 24th (WRB AB DT CJH AMcI IW).
F   50 ->NW Kinneil 9 Aug (DT).
C   Large numbers in autumn at dusk around Tullibody Inch, though did
not always roost: 6000 on 21 Aug & 3000 on 23rd (but only 100 on
31st); 2200 on 6 Sep, 5000 on 14th, 8000 on 18th (MVB CJH).
SWP   3 Prs nested Ashfield (WRB). 11 AoT per sq Km on Doune CBC (NB).

HOUSE MARTIN *Delichon urbica (B)*
1st records, much earlier than usual: 1 Airthrey 4 Apr, 2 Denny on 6th, 1
Dunblane on 7th & 1 Carronshore on 9th (MVB BDA BH AB); widespread in
last week of April. Last: 28 Menstrie on 17 Sep & 6 on 18th (BRT BH).
S   Carron Valley Res: 8 nests at east houses & 7 at west houses (AVB).
SWP   6 nests Ashfield (WRB). 24 nests per sq Km on Doune CBC, double
1994 (NB). 55 Doune Ponds 13 Aug (AD).

TREE PIPIT *Anthus trivialis (B)*
1st records: L.Chon-Kinlochard (abundant) 18 April, Carron Valley Forest on
27th, Rhuveag & Glen Buckie on 30th; Plean CP & Dunblane on 1 May (WRB

BDA DT HMR NB).
F   6 Dunmore Moss 6 May (DT).

MEADOW PIPIT *Anthus pratensis (B,W)*
F   16 Skinflats 16 Mar to 50 on 22 Apr (AB).
C   17 on Ochils at 400m 17Feb (BRT); 150 Ben Cleuch 23 Sep (WRB).
S   130 N Third Res 21 Sep & 61 -> SSW on 29th (CJH).
SWP   Widespread in young plantations Glen Ogle16 Sep. 6 at 500m Ledard
        Glen 19 Nov & 35 at 310m Craig Innich 17 Dec - late for hills. 54
        Arnieve 14 Dec (CJH).

*ROCK PIPIT *Anthus petrosus (w)*
F   1 Blackness on 2 Jan & 2 on 7 Oct. 2 Skinflats (Kinc.Br.) 23 Dec (CJH
        DT).

*YELLOW WAGTAIL *Motacilla flava*
F   1 of Blueheaded race *M.f.flava* at Kinneil 12 May, associated with Pied
        & White Wagtails. M *M.f.flavissima* at Skinflats 16 May (GO).

GREY WAGTAIL *Motacilla cinerea (B,w)*
        Winter records (Jan-Feb, Nov-Dec): 1 Cambus 1 Jan, 2 Kinneil on 2nd, 1
        Cambuskenneth on 12th & 1 Hillhead on 19th, 2 BoA 1 Feb & 1 Kinneil on
        4th; 2 Stirling from 16 Oct & 2 Alva.from 21st, 1 Dunblane in Dec & 1
        Carronshore on 2nd (CJH AB TDS DT PMA BH).
C   2 AoT on Devon at Cambus 15 Apr (BDA). Pair Menstrie 8 May (DAC).
S   1 Plean CP 13 Apr (HMR). 2 N.Third Res 28 Apr, feeding young on 27
        May (GB BDA).
SWP   2 AoT Ashfield (WRB). Bred Dunblane (BH). In breeding season at
        Ledard Glen, Buchlyvie, Arnprior, Doune CBC, Blairdrummond
        (DAC NB JT). Widespread in Sep with 3 at Gart on 19th (NB).

PIED WAGTAIL *Motacilla alba (B, w)*
F   Skinflats: 13 on 14 Jan, 20 on 13 Apr, 20 on 29th Oct. 10 Kinneil 2 Jan
        (CJH AB). 8 Slamannan 19 Jan (TDS). White Wagtails *M.a.alba* - 3
        Skinflats on 13 Apr, 17 on 20th & 2 on 28th, 5 Kinneil on 1 May (AB
        GO DT).
C   3 AoT on Devon CBS (CJH).
S   100 at Airthrey roost 19 Sep & 236 on 4 Dec (CJH). 147 at BoA meat
        plant 26 Nov left E at dusk - possibly to Airthrey roost (MVB). 2 AoT
        L.Arklet (WRB).
SWP   22 in muddy root crop Braes of Doune10 Feb. 7 AoT at Doune CBC,
        increase, 1st fledged 30 May (NB). 70 at roost Thornhill 4 Jul (SS). 30
        Glen Lochay 1 Oct (PWS).

DIPPER *Cinclus cinclus (B,W)*
        Greatly underercorded.
F   1 Polmont 27 Dec (JW).
C   Singing on Devon CBS 8 Feb but absent in summer (CJH).
S   2 on Allan at Haws Park, BoA 1 Feb (CJH).
SWP   2 pairs on Allan Water at Dunblane 26 Mar, Juvs seen from 14 May
        (BH). 1 pair on Doune CBC (NB).

WREN *Troglodytes troglodytes (B,W)*
Under-recorded (Ed).
C   14 AoT on 5 Km of lower Devon (CJH).
S   22 M territories & 18 F in 14 Ha of Mine Wood (M.Evans).
SWP 11 Pairs per sq Km Doune CBC (up x4 on 1994, NB). No change on
     Blairdrummond spring transect. Singing at 500m in Ledard Glen 19
     Nov (CJH).

HEDGE SPARROW *Accentor modularis (B,W)*
Under-recorded (Ed).
C   6 AoT on 5 Km of lower Devon (CJH).
SWP 9.6 pair per sq Km on Doune CBC (up x2 on 1994). 12th commonest
     · species through year in Dunblane garden (NB).

ROBIN *Erithacus rubecula (B,W)*
Under-recorded (Ed)
C   5 AoT on 5 Km of lower Devon (CJH).
SWP Spring numbers much as 1994 on Blairdrummond transect (CJH). 6
     pairs per sq Km on Doune CBC (up x4 on 1994). 2nd commonest
     species through year in Dunblane garden (NB).

REDSTART *Phoenicurus phoenicurus (B)*
F   1 Skinflats 8 Sep & 1 on 17th (AB GO).
C   Bred Woodhill, Dollar Glen (MC). 1 Gartmorn 30 Jul (WB).
S   1 AoT Sauchieburn 30 May (BDA).
SWP 49 nest attempts at Trossachs colony reared 204 Y (HR). 1 L.Ard 16 Apr
     (WRB), 3 Rhuveag (Balquhidder) on 30th (DT), also 6 AoT in summer
     at L.Chon (WRB).

WHINCHAT *Saxicola rubetra (B)*
Under-recorded as breeding (Ed).
1st records: 1 Flanders Moss 21 Apr, Carron Valley Res on 27th, Cromlix on
     28th, 3 Glen Buckie on 30th, pair Skinflats 3 May (SS BDA WRB DT).
F   Probably bred Skinflats, 6 Juv on 14 Aug, last on 10 Sep (RS MVB). 1
     Jupiter WG on 7 May, 1st record for site (RS).
C   2 family parties Menstrie Glen 2 Aug (WRB).
S   5 AoT Stronachlachar 10 Jun (WRB). Pair + 6Y L.Arklet 16 Jul (BDA).
SWP 1 pair on Doune CBC - not seen before 24 May (NB).

*STONECHAT *Saxicola torquata (b,w)*
Distinct signs of sustained population increase (Ed).
F   Slamannan: Pair L.Ellrig 13 Jan & M on 31st, M Garbethill 8 Mar, M
     Newcraig 24 Dec (TDS AMcI). Imm Skinflats 16 Jun, imm M on 22 Oct
     (GO MVB AB).
C   Pair Alva Glen in Apr, + 2Y on 29 Aug (WRB).
S   1 Earlshill 1 Jan, 1 Touch Res 16 Apr, M Kippen Muir 28 Oct (WRB IW
     CJH). Pair carrying food Cringate Muir 11 Jun (GO).
SWP M at 400m Monachyle Glen 1 Apr, 3 AoT Hutchison Ptn in May, Pair
     + 3 Juv L.Arklet 15 Jul (WRB). 1 Ledard Glen 20 Jun (JT), Juv Glen

Finglas 30 Aug, M Glengyle 19 Nov (DAC). Imm Gart 26 Sep, 2 Drumloist 21 Oct, Pair above L.Ard 19 Nov - edge of Ptn at 300m (CJH).

WHEATEAR *Oenanthe oenanthe (B)*
Under-recorded as breeding in C, S, SWP (Ed).
1st records: 1 Kinneil 1 Apr, 2 N.Third Res on 2nd, 1 Skinflats & 2 Hutchinson Moor on 8th, F Kippen Muir on 9th, 4 Touch Res on 16th (AB BDA DT WRB DAC, IW); 5 on arable at Doune CBC, 6 Dunmore 3 May & up to 3 Skinflats & Kinneil 1-12 May were migrants (NB GB DT GO). Last 1 Bannockburn 8 Oct (DT).
F   Imm appeared at Kinneil 9 July & Skinflats on 11th (DT GO).
S   2 Earlsburn 27 Apr (BDA). 3 AoT L.Arklet in summer (WRB).
SWP   3 AoT Stronachlachar-Glengyle 10 Jun (WRB), bred Kinbuck (MVB) Pair + Y Glen Lochay 24 Jul (PWS).

*RING OUSEL *Turdus torquatus (b)*
S   M Lees Hill (Gargunnocks) 25 Apr (MT).
SWP   2 AoT Monachyle Glen 22 Apr (DOE). 2 Rhuveag 30 Apr (DT). 2M Glengyle 18 May (DOE), 1 L.Arklet on 23rd (WRB).

BLACKBIRD *Turdus merula (B,W)*
C   10 AoT on 5 Km of lower Devon (CJH).
SWP   Max Dunblane 12 in Jul (BH), 3rd commonest garden species (NB). 19.2 pairs per sq Km on Doune CBC, fledglings from 2 Jun (NB). 10 - > S Glen Dochart 12 Dec (PWS).

FIELDFARE *Turdus pilaris (W)*
F   300 Garbethill 1 Jan, 300 Skinflats on 2nd & 250 Slamannan on 18th (TDS DT AMcI). 1st of autumn 1 Slamannan 11 Oct (TDS).
S   400 Lossburn Res 21 Apr (IW).
SWP   500 L.Macanrie & 200 Blairdrummond carse 22 Jan, 80 Lecropt 26 Feb, 150 Drip Carse 4 Mar & 200 Gartmore on 22nd, 300 Thornhill 9 Apr & 250 Kinbuck on 18th (DT NB MVB CJH WRB). Last, 1 Doune 5 May (BDA).
        Late arrival in autumn, 1st at Ashfield 1 Nov, many Glen Lochay on 8th, 15 -> SW Airthrey on 14th, 60 Glengyle on 19th & hundreds Stronend on 28th; 200 Hutchison 21 Dec (WRB PWS DMB DAC RJ).

SONG THRUSH *Turdus philomelos (B,W)*
Under-recorded as breeding (Ed).
C   3 AoT in 5 Km lower Devon (CJH).
S   20 , with Redwings, Plean CP 29 Oct (AB).
SWP   A few wintered on Allan Water at Dunblane, max 6 on 18 Mar (BH). 2 in spring on Hill House BBS, Braes of Doune (WRB). 2 pairs on Doune CBC; 1 through Nov-Dec Dunblane (NB).

REDWING *Turdus iliacus (W)*
A late and spasmodic autumn immigration (Ed).
F   50 Garbethill 5 Jan; 1st of autumn at Slamannan 11 Oct (TDS).

C   280 Cambus 9 Dec (CJH).
S   30 Plean CP 23 Jan (HMR). 15 Stirling 15 Oct (IW), 20 -> S Airthrey on
     16th & 390 ->W on 31st (DMB MVB). 250 -> NW BoA 31 Oct, 10 ->
     N on 8 Nov (CJH). Hundreds Stronend 28 Nov (RJ).
SWP 65 Doune 29 Jan (AD). 65 -> NW Braes of Doune 21 Oct, 70 -> S
     Dunblane on 23rd, 500 L.Venachar on 25th, 22 -> S Pass of Leny on
     29th (CJH MVB). Small flocks Glen Lochay 21 Oct, more on 8 Nov
     (PWS). 90 Lecropt 26 Nov & 100 Hutchison 21 Dec (MVB WRB).
     Flocks of 50 at L.Spling & L.Katrine 22 Nov & at L.Voil on 28th (NB).

*MISTLE THRUSH *Turdus viscivorus (B,W)*
Under-recorded, but probably getting scarcer (Ed)
S   5 Carron valley Res 6 Oct (AB).
SWP 2 L.Arklet 16 Apr (WRB). 10 Glen Lochay 1 Sep, 17 Braes of Doune 22
     Sep, 7 Pass of Leny 29 Oct; 1 -> S Glen Dochart 12 Dec (PWS CJH).

*GRASSHOPPER WARBLER *Locustella naevia (b)*
Seems to have become scarce in last few years (Ed)
F   1 Skinflats 28 Apr, present to 14 Jul with 2 singing on 6 May (BDA AB
     RS GO). 1 singing Carronshore 1 May & 27 Jul (AB).
SWP 1 Drip carse 13 Jun (BDA), 2 Flanders Moss in Aug (TJ).

SEDGE WARBLER *Acrocephalus schoenobaenus (B)*
Under-recorded as breeder (Ed)
F   Skinflats: 2 on 1 May & 8 on 13th (GO). 1 Kinneil on 4 May, 19 singing
     on 21st (GO DT).1 Dunmore 4 May (GB), 1 on R.Carron at Larbert 11
     Jun (JW).
C   2 AoT Cambus (WRB). 54 AoT on Devon WBS, none on 29 Apr but
     most arrived by 9 May, imitated calls of Oystercatcher, Redshank,
     Common Sandpiper, Swallow, Pied Wagtail, Willow Warbler,
     Chaffinch, Reed Bunting; marked decline in song by end May (CJH).
S   2 singing Cowie 6 May (DT). Singing along Forth at Arnprior on 24
     Jun wherever cover present (CJH).
SWP 1 singing Corriarklet 6 May (WRB).

*LESSER WHITETHROAT *Sylvia curruca (?b)*
S   M singing Stirling (Broomridge) 2 May to 17th, in dense scrub with
     much hawthorn, no F seen (DT).

WHITETHROAT *Sylvia communis (B)*
1st records: 1 Skinflats 3 May (5 on 6th), Carronshore on 4th ; 5 Cowie & 8
     Dunmore on 6th, Buchlyvie on 7th, Blairlogie on 8th, Doune on 10th
     (GO AB DT DAC NB).
C   9 AoT on Devon WBS (CJH). Pair feeding Y Myretoun Hill 2 Aug
     (WRB).
SWP 13.2 pairs per sq Km Doune CBC, 1st on 10 May, fledglings from 20
     Jun (NB). 2 AoT Ashfield, 1 AoT Laighills (WRB BH). 2 AoT in deep
     heather L.Arklet 26 Jun (WRB).

GARDEN WARBLER *Sylvia borin (B)*
F   3 Dunmore 5 May (GB).
SWP   1st Laighhills 14 May, probably 3 AoT (BH). 2 AoT Ashfield (WRB).

BLACKCAP *Sylvia atricapilla (B)*
Under-recorded as breeder (Ed)
Winter records: 1 Dunblane 5 Jan to mid Feb, 1 Thornhill 6 Jan, Pair Alva 13 Jan to 11 Apr, 1 Falkirk 19 Jan, M Blairlogie 1 Feb; F Skinflats 10 Nov, M Alva 3 Dec, 3 (2M) BoA 28 Nov to 30 Dec; birds seen to eat apple & snowberry (AD B.Howe PMA J.Anusas GO DMB CJH KD)
F   1 R.Carron at Denny 10 Jun (JW). M Skinflats 12 May, 3 birds on 7 Jul (GO).
S   Pair with nest material Plean CP 30 Apr (AB). Song Balquhidderock Wood 2 Jun (DT)
SWP   1 AoT L.Chon (WRB).

WOOD WARBLER *Phylloscopus sibilatrix (B)*
C   3 AoT Cowpark (MC).
S   Several AoT Mine Wood (WRB).
SWP   3 Lake of Menteith 8 May (DT). Song widespread L.Chon in May (WRB).

CHIFFCHAFF *Phylloscopus collybita (B)*
1st records: Plean CP 2 Apr, Invertrossachs on 3rd, Hermitage Wood on 4th, Dunmore on 7th, Bo'ness & Menteith Hills on 12th (DT RAB CJH GB RS). Last Stirling 19 Sep (RJ).
F   6 Dunmore Wood 9 May, left by end Aug (GB). 2 Castle Cary May, last on 1 Sep (BDA). 1 Larbert 30 Apr (JW).
C   Spring/summer at Redcarr Wood, Cambus, Alva, Alloa, Kennetpans (BRT BDA WRB).
S   Song Torwood 23 Apr (AB).
SWP   Spring/summer at Dunblane, Thornhill (L.Dhu), Aberfoyle, Kinlochard, Glassert (BH DT WRB).

WILLOW WARBLER *Phylloscopus trochilus (B)*
1st records: Airthrey 12 Apr, Menteith Hills on 13th, Devon (7) on 14th, Kinneil & Carronshore on 15th, Buchlyvie & Dunblane on 16th, Doune on 17th; all Devon population in by 29 Apr (DMB DT CJH BDA AB DAC BH NB). Last, singles at Skinflats on 11 Sep & Carron Valley Res on 12th (AB AKM).
F   Regular at Dunmore Moss to 18 Aug, when large fire; 9 AoT Dunmore Wood 31 May, visited garden from 17 Jul to mid Aug (GB).
C   14 AoT on 5Km of lower Devon (CJH).
S   Feeding flock of 7 BoA 7 Aug (DMB).
SWP   3.6 pairs per sq Km on Doune CBC (NB). Probably 4 AoT Laighills in May, last on 22 Aug (BH). 15 with Tits Dunblane 6 Sep (MVB). No change in summer records on Blairdrummond transect (CJH).

GOLDCREST *Regulus regulus (B,W)*
Greatly under-recorded (Ed)
F   Skinflats: present through year, 9 on 5 Nov (AB GO). At Dunmore

CARRION CROW *Corvus corone (B,W)*
F   55 Kinneil 24 Sep (CJH).Carrion/Hoodie hybrid Slamannan 26 Oct (TDS).
C   Cambus roost: 160 on 3 Jan (CJH).
SWP 24 Sheriffmuir 24 Sep (MVB). Numbers much as 1994 on Blairdrummond BBS transect. 46 Ward Toll (1 Hoodie) 29 Mar. 65 (2 dark hybrids) L.Ard 19 Nov (CJH). Hoodies: 1 feeding Dunblane centre 19 Jul (AD). In breeding range at L.Dochart, L.Voil & Balquhidder (10 hybrids out of 13), Lake of Menteith, L.Rusky, L.Chon, L.Arklet, L.Venachar, L.Lubnaig (NB).

RAVEN *Corvus corax (B,W)*
C   2 Ben Cleuch 13 Aug (WRB). 2 Dumyat 9 Mar (AMcI).
S   4 territories checked, 3 pairs; 4 pairs successful of which 3 pairs reared 9Y (PSA).4 Carron V Forest 29 Sep & 2 on 30 Nov (TDS AKM). 2 Kippen Muir 14 Jan & 2 L.Laggan 8 Feb (DAC NB). 2 Stronend 28 Oct (CJH).
SWP 8 territories checked, 7 pairs; 2 successful pairs reared 8Y (PSA). 27 Ardoch Burn mid-May (WRB). 3 north of Doune 8 Oct & 7 L.Mahaick 8 Nov (DAC NB). On low ground: 2 Thornhill 7 Feb, 7 on 8 Mar & 5 on 9 Sep (SS). 1 Arnieve 14 Dec . Out of usual breeding area: 2 L.Ard Forest Feb-Apr (CJH).

STARLING *Sturnus vulgaris (B,W)*
F   400 Slamannan 18 Jan (AMcI). 40 at Jun-Jul roost Dunmore (GB). 400 Kinneil 3 Sep (AB). 2000 roost Kincardine Bridge 18 Nov (CJH).
C   Tullibody Inch roost: 250 on 30 Jul, 1100 on 23 Aug, roost flights in area 120 on 14 Jul & 800 on 20 Aug; a roost flight on 17 Nov was attended by Kestrel, Peregrine and Sparrowhawk (CJH MVB)
S   2200 at roost Stirling centre 24 Jan to 13 Feb (DT).
SWP 12 pairs per sq Km on Doune CBC, fledglings from 23 May - 10 days earlier than 1994. 3rd commonest species in Dunblane garden, max 25 (NB).

HOUSE SPARROW *Passer domesticus (B,W)*
Under-recorded (Ed).
F   40 Letham peat factory from Jun (GB).
C   80 in wheatfield Alva 15 Jul (CJH).
SWP 22.8 pairs per sq Km on Doune CBC. 7th commonest species in Dunblane garden, max 12 (NB). Max 28 Ashfield (WRB), 10 Dunblane 8 Dec (BH). 10 Killin 22 Aug & 26 Nov (PWS).

TREE SPARROW *Passer montanus (B,W)*
F   3 Blackness 21Jan (WRB). 20 Skinflats 8 Jan, 4 Carronshore 24 Dec (AB). 25 Airth 1 Nov (IW). Pair reared 2 broods N.Doll (GB).
C   30 Kennetpans 29 Jan (MC). 5 Gartmorn 7 Feb to 6 Aug (WB PMA).
S   32 Cambusbarron 6 Apr (WRB).
SWP 90 Lecropt 28 Jan, 50 on 3 Mar & 55 on 30 Dec (MVB). 12 Thornhill carse 19 Mar & 28 Oct (DAC). 1 Dunblane 25 Apr (NB).

CHAFFINCH *Fringilla coelebs (B,W)*
F　　150 Blackness 21 Jan (WRB).
C　　13 AoT on lower Devon in May (CJH).
S　　100 Blairlogie 16 Jan (BRT). 400 in rape stubble Pendreich 12 Mar & 300 on 21 Oct (CJH).
SWP　34.8 pairs per sq Km on Doune CBC - commonest species (NB). 40% fewer on Blairdrummond spring BBS transect (CJH). 200 Killin 21 Nov (PWS). Large flock Dunblane 12 Oct (BH). 250 Drip carse 2 Dec, 150 Lecropt on 9th & 180 Kinbuck on 10th (MVB DT WRB).

BRAMBLING *Fringilla montifringilla (W)*
F　　1 Kinneil 2 Jan (DT). 3 Dunmore Jan to Mar (GB). 6 records Slamannan 18 Oct to 14 Dec (TDS).
C　　7 Gartmorn Jan-Feb, 3 on 15 Apr (MC WB).
SWP　1 Dunblane 2 & 5 Mar & 2 Doune on 13th (NB MVB RAB). Singles Ashfield in Oct (WRB).

GREENFINCH *Carduelis chloris (B,W)*
F　　150 Kinneil 9 Sep & 160 on 17th (DT CJH). 200 N.Doll 10 Oct (GB).
SWP　3.6 pairs per sq Km on Doune CBC. 7th commonest species in Dunblane garden, max 11 (NB). 100 Thornhill carse 8 Oct (DAC).

GOLDFINCH *Carduelis carduelis (B,W)*
F　　Skinflats: Max 47 on 15 Apr, 20 on 7-20 Dec (BDA AB). 20 Kinneil 26 Feb (DT). A few Polmont through year (JW). 9 Dunmore 15 Jan, 1 AoT on Moss (CJH GB).
C　　8 Tullibody Inch 10 Jan, 30 Cambus 9 Sep 7 & 10 on 28 Dec. 7 Diverswell 8 Apr (CJH BRT).
S　　4 Carron bridge 30 Jan (WRB). 8 Plean CP 13 Feb (HMR).
SWP　7.2 pairs per sq Km on Doune CBC (NB). 1 L.Arklet 18 Apr. 10 Kinbuck 10 Dec & 19 Cromlix on 17th (WRB).

SISKIN *Carduelis spinus (B,W)*
F　　M Skinflats 28 Apr (AB). 2 at feeder Dunmore in May (GB).
S　　1 BoA 14 May, no evidence nesting (CJH). lst of autumn in Stirling garden 28 Oct (D&RJ).
SWP　Max 5 in Dunblane garden (NB). Last in Dunblane on 2 May (BH). In summer at L.Dhu (Rusky), Rhuveag, Glen Buckie, Menteith Hills (DT). 35 Dunblane 6 Sep (MVB). 20 Glen Lochay 9 Sep, 100 L.Tay 24 Oct & 100 Killin 4 Dec (PWS). 80 L.Venachar 25 Oct & 30 Glen Finglas 10 Dec (CJH).

LINNET *Carduelis cannabina (B,W)*
F　　60 Slamannan 10 Mar (TDS). 110 Kinneil 27 Aug,140 on 17 Sep & 220 on 23 Dec (CJH). 40 Skinflats 6 Oct (AB).
C　　80 Alva pools 7 Feb (CJH). 85 Gartmorn Jan-Feb (MC). 53 Kennetpans 10 Sep (CJH).
S　　400 in stubble Blairlogie 16 Jan (BRT).
SWP　100 Lecropt 1 Jan & 250 on 26 Feb (DT MVB). 7.2 Pairs per sq Km on Doune CBC (NB). 240 Arnieve 20 Dec (CJH).

TWITE *Carduelis flavirostris (b,W)*
F   20 Skinflats 20 Dec (AB). 15 Kinneil 26 Feb & 20 on 4 Mar (DT BDA). 53 Airth shore 3 Dec (CJH).
C   3 by Devon at Alva 26 May (CJH). in Ochils: 2 Balquharn Burn 4 Aug, 2 Craighorn on 6th & 65 on Marsh Thistles Greenhorn Burn on 8th (WRB).
S   1 Gargunnock 25 Apr (MT). 12 Carron Valley Res 5 Oct (TDS).
SWP 1 or 2 pairs in Apr-Jun at Severie (Braes of Doune), Ben Uamha, Glengyle, L.Arklet (WRB BDA).

REDPOLL *Carduelis flammea (B,W)*
S   20 Plean CP 19 Oct (HMR). 35 Carron Valley Forest 30 Nov (AKM). 15 BoA 19 Dec (KD).
SWP 3 Ledard Glen 20 Jun (JT). 2 AoT Hutchinson Ptn in Jun (WRB). Pair + 2 Juv L.Arklet 16 Jul (BDA). 100 Killin 4 Dec (PWS). 70 in birches L.Katrine 15 Dec & 10 Dunblane on 25th (NB).

BULLFINCH *Pyrrhula pyrrhula (B,W)*
F   10 Slamannan (Newcraig) 2 Jan (TDS). 12 Dunmore Wood 17 Nov (GB).
S   Feeding on seed of Hypericum at Stirling Jan & Mar, at peanuts 30 Apr (D&RJ).
SWP 6 Glen Finglas 10 Dec & 5 Hutchinson Ptn on17th (CJH WRB).

COMMON CROSSBILL *Loxia curvirostra (b,W)*
S   10 Carron Valley Forest 4 Nov, M in song on 30th (AKM).
SWP 7 Torrie Forest 1 Jan (DT). 1 Aberfoyle quarries 2 Apr & 17 on 26 Nov, 1 L.Ard Forest 22 Jun (CJH).

HAWFINCH *Coccothraustes coccothraustes (?b,?w)*
No records received

*SNOW BUNTING *Plectrophenax nivalis (W)*
No records received from the the the winter hills (Ed)
F   1 Slamannan 24 Nov (TDS).
S   1 Sheriffmuir 5 Mar (SS).

YELLOWHAMMER *Emberiza citrinella (B,W)*
F   35 Blackness 21 Jan (WRB). 27 Airth shore 6 Jan & 30 Skinflats shore 23 Dec (CJH). 2 AoT Dunmore Moss in May (GB).
C   125 Gartmorn Jan-Feb (MC). 118 Menstrie 28 Feb (BRT). 8 Aot in 5 km on lower Devon (CJH).
SWP 19.2 pairs per sq Km on Doune CBC (NB). Numbers unchanged at Blairdrummond BBS May-June. 112 Arnieve 30 Dec (CJH). Now few around Dunblane (BH). 1 Killin 22 Nov - very scarce here (PWS).

REED BUNTING *Emberiza schoeniclus (B,W)*
F   3 Polmont 3 Jan fed on seeds of Pampas Grass (JW). 40 Skinflats 2 Jan, 2 AoT 12 May (DT BDA). 4 AoT Kinneil 15 Apr (BDA). Frequent on Letham Moss in May (GB). 9 Airth shore 6 Jan & 8 Dunmore 11 Nov (CJH GB).

C   1 AoT Cambus Pool 12 Apr. 10 Aot on Devon WBS (CJH).
S   2 AoT west Carron Valley Res (AKM). Nest Chartershall 30 May
       (BDA).
SWP   15 Lecropt 2 Jan (MVB). 4 L.Arklet 14 Apr. 1 AoT Ashfield (WRB). 1
       pair on Doune CBC (NB).
*CORN BUNTING *Miliaria calandra (b,w)*
F   M Singing Powfoulis 5 May (GO).

ESCAPED SPECIES

SNOW GOOSE *Anser caerulescens*
S   1 (blue phase) Alloa Inch 9 Apr (DMB) -*possibly the resident bird from
       NorthThird ? (Ed).*

MANDARIN *Aix galericulata*
SWP   1 L.Watston 9 Sep (CJH). Drake in moult to full plumage, bill colour
       suggests a bird of the year. lst record for area, almost certainly an
       escape from a wildfowl collection.

RED-LEGGED/CHUKAR PARTRIDGE *Alectoris chukar*
F   7 Garbethill Muir 5 Feb (BDA).

GUINEA FOWL *Numida meleagris*
SWP   5 Kippenross 12 Mar, 3 with white on breast (CJH).

COCKATIEL *Nymphicus hollandicus*
S   1 Airthrey 13 Sep (DMB).

WILDFOWL REPORT (1995-96)

The organiser for the inland waters part of this area's Wetlands and Estuary
Bird Survey (WEBS) is Neil Bielby, he reports that two more still water sites
were covered this season, most notably the head of Loch Tay at Killin. A major
developement in this survey was the counting of about one third of the non-
estuarine river system. The main concentrations and monthly distribution of
waterfowl were similar to 1994, with Gartmorn Dam retaining its pre-
eminence; however Lochs Ard and Venachar showed considerable increases
and moved into the top ten list, whilst the Carron Valley Reservoir decreased
by 33% and fell to 9th place. In this area sections of the Rivers Forth, Teith and
Devon were counted and were especially important for Cormorant, Whooper
Swan, Wigeon and Teal.

Using the WEBS data for still water (non-river) sites, an interesting
comparison can be made between the lowland region of Stirling and
Clackmannan and the highland lochs north of the carse of Stirling. The data
are in the following table:

Comparison of Wildfowl on Lowland and Highland waters

Date:		Sep	Oct	Nov	Dec	Jan	Feb	Mar	Total
Little Grebe	L	36	17	5			2	8	68
	H	23	5	10	10	13	11	13	85
Gr.Cr.Grebe	L	9	6	6	3	2	2	17	45
	H						1		1
Cormorant	L	20	16	6	11	10	16	5	84
	H	4	12	20	1	8	7	2	54
MuteSwan	L	68	103	49	93	43	66	74	496
	H	9	8	10	7	11	7	8	60
Whooper Swan	L			5	12	3	8	5	33
	H		7	30	66	25	36	18	182
Wigeon	L	69	100	449	1559	1019	594	507	4580
	H	29	10	51	117	101	17	63	388
Teal	L	19	168	160	341	158	176	145	1167
	H	13	54	83	145	80	40	47	462
Mallard	L	2144	2515	2325	1644	1669	1402	764	12463
	H	493	515	908	767	591	444	243	3961
Pochard	L	10	94	23	54	36	49	51	317
	H		52	117	144	189	138	54	694
Tufted Duck	L	232	268	346	239	147	211	236	1679
	H		13	37	39	30	15	14	148
Goldeneye	L	2	9	141	101	95	125	206	669
	H		7	54	56	75	101	111	404
Goosander	L	3	47	6	7	10	16	10	99
	H	56	13	30	25	15	19	21	179
Coot	L	233	762	814	765	479	528	289	3870
	H	1	1		1	5		1	9

Great Crested Grebes are almost entirely restricted to lowland waters and show a marked arrival in March, by contrast Little Grebes are commoner in the highlands and remain in numbers there throughout the winter. Mute Swans are scarce in the highlands whilst their fluctuations in the lowlands probably reflect local dispersal onto rivers. The Whooper Swan results are rather misleading since there are large groups feeding on fields on the carses. Both Wigeon and Teal are mainly lowland species and build up in numbers between September and December, remaining common into March. The fairly steady numbers of lowland Mallard through autumn and early winter reflect released birds and their artificial feeding, however in the highlands there is a marked November peak likely to be the arrival of immigrants. A comparison of Pochard and Tufted Duck shows quite different preference patterns and only Pochard have a marked influx (October - which parallels other observations in the species account). Goldeneye show no strong preference and have a main arrival in November and further increases in February-March, a unique seasonal pattern. In contrast, Goosanders peak in early autumn, except that other notes also show an April influx to the estuary; it would be interesting to study the relative frequency of adult males. Finally, Coot are an extreme lowland specialist but show a striking October increase at the two main wintering sites, many of these birds are likely to be from the continent.

WEBS contributors to these data additional to report list were: M.Adam, R.Chapman, M.Hamilton, S.Harley, A.Hibbert, W.McEwan, R.Nudds, D.Series, D.Shenton, A.Theil.

REVIEWS AND NOTES (Naturalist)

Soils: Scotland's Living Landscape. Andrew Taylor and Stephen Nortcliff. Scottish Natural Heritage. 1996. 24pp. ISBN 1.85397.223.1. £2.50.

An authoritative introduction – what is soil, its importance and history. The Scottish landscapes soils: Uplands, Central Lowlands, Highlands, East Coast, the Islands. A handsome colour illustrated production.

Safe to Drink? The Quality of Your Water. Julie Stauffer. New Futures 9. Centre for Alternative Technology. 160pp. ISBN 1.898049.19.X. £7.95.

A Canadian biologist researching water and waste waters contributes here to one of over 20 books in a series aimed by CAT to empower people with practical, positive ways to improve their knowledge and understanding of the environment e.g. The Food Cycle, Water Power, Solar Power, Transport. The author covers sources of water, how it is treated, where it goes, how managed, effects of privatisation, costs, is there enough? ... and includes sources of information as a 15-page resources guide, and index. Some highlights include: a 1994 survey of children under five found a majority no longer drink water – partly as parents fear tap water is not good enough: the provision of good clean water has been the single greatest achievement in public health in the last two centuries: now there are questions – will market-driven forces provide the best public benefits and have the public regulators the ability to ensure they do: since privatisation in 1990 capital investment in new plant and distribution has gone down by £282m (10%) where government reasoning was to increase investment: profits up 36%: boardroom salaries up £540,000 to £2.4m (440%): annual cost of providing to consumers up £294m (12%). A thoughtful contribution to water studies.

In the *Glasgow Naturalist* **23(1)** pp58-9 are short notes of interest by John Mitchell on Pillwort and *Limosella aquatica* L at Loch Lomond, and Dual trees on Inchloanaig by John Proctor.

INVERSNAID RSPB NATURE RESERVE - THE FIRST TEN YEARS

M. Trubridge, RSPB

In 1986 the Royal Society for the Protection of Birds purchased 923 acres of mountain, moorland and woodland on the north east side of Loch Lomond, specifically to acquire part of the Loch Lomond woods Site of Special Scientific Interest (SSSI). This is considered to be the most important semi-natural deciduous woodland complex in the south of Scotland. These few remaining woodlands are the last relics of the extensive natural forest that once covered over half the country. They are not only areas of outstandingly beautiful countryside, but they are also an important and irreplaceable natural resource. It is possible to trace the history of these woods right back to the original forests that grew at the end of the last Ice Age. Unlike commercial forestry, they have had 10,000 years of adaptation to the Scottish environment and contain a much greater variety of plants and wildlife. Today, native woodlands account for only 1% of Scotland's land cover and this country has a lower proportion of tree cover than any other country in Europe, except Iceland.

The decline in native woodland has accelerated recently and since the Second World War Britain has lost about 40% of its tree cover. In some areas, such as Glen Garry in Lochaber, losses have been as high as 64%. Such losses resulted in the development of new policies to protect deciduous woodland in the mid 1980s by the Forestry Commission. However, the problems facing many of our woodlands have not been diminished by the Commission's commendable actions. Woodlands are still heavily grazed in many areas and are continuing to decline in size, quality and structure.

Such a situation faced the RSPB when it purchased Inversnaid Estate in 1986. In the early days it became clear that there was an extremely low level of successful natural regeneration of any trees due to the presence of large numbers of deer, feral goats and sheep. A botanical survey in 1987 found substantial regeneration to the seedling stage but no sapling recruitment due to excessive levels of grazing and browsing. Like any other resource, the Inversnaid woodlands need to be managed properly in order to survive for future generations. So when the Society drew up its Management Plan for the reserve, one of the key policies was to lower the levels of overgrazing by reducing the numbers of herbivores present on the site.

The deer are being controlled through the time honoured custom of deerstalking, with the Society using professional stalkers. Every winter between 15 and 35 red deer are shot on the reserve, and occasionally one or two roe deer. It may sound strange for a conservation body to be shooting wildlife, but there are times when this is the only practical solution. There is now no natural predator of deer in Britain, with the wolf having been exterminated over 200 years ago. Therefore it is up to man to carry out the cull necessary to keep deer numbers in balance.

The control of deer at Inversnaid is part of a wider management of red deer numbers in the area organised by the Balquhidder Deer Management Group, under the auspices of the Red Deer Commission. This has resulted in a reduction of the red deer population on the reserve, particularly during the winter months. From a maximum of 94 in the winter of 1987/8, numbers have decreased to a maximum of 43 in 1993/4 and 28 in 1994/5. Usually there are no more than 20-30 animals present in the winter, with half that figure during the summer, a considerable improvement on ten years ago.

The second major herbivore are feral goats (Figure 1). The goats at Inversnaid, and indeed at many other locations throughout Scotland, are neither wild nor native animals. Their history is a complex affair and at times it is difficult to separate fact from fiction. Certainly there have been goats in the Loch Lomond area for a long time, although some of them are descended from a herd of milking goats kept at an army camp near Loch Ard during the First World War. Unfortunately goats are one of the most destructive animals known and at Inversnaid it is the woodland that is suffering from their grazing, browsing and bark stripping activities.

Initially the RSPB reduced their numbers by rounding up small groups and exporting them to goat farmers in Scotland. This appeared to work quite well for three years, until concern was expressed that gathering goats with dogs caused unacceptable stress to the animals. It was suggested by a number of people, including the Scottish Society for the Prevention of Cruelty to Animals, that shooting the goats was a more humane method of control. However, when this technique was first used in November 1990, further controversy ensued. As a result, a moratorium was imposed on goat control while an independent assessment was carried out on the goat population by an outside expert. His lengthy report, published in 1993, recommended that the Inversnaid herd should be maintained at the specified limits of a maximum of 50 (no more than 25 females) and a minimum of 30 (no less than 15 females), with shooting being the preferred culling technique. This has now been accepted by most people and goat control now takes place on an annual basis in exactly the same way as deer are controlled.

The final herbivore in the grazing equation are sheep. They were more or less excluded from the reserve area some 30 years ago with the erection of a march fence on the eastern boundary. It is interesting to note that at about this time a few birch trees developed on the open moorland. Undoubtedly the substantial decline in sheep numbers enabled some natural regeneration to occur for a while. However, when the RSPB took over the property in 1986, there were still up to 90 stray animals on the reserve. They were gaining access along the unfenced northern boundary. In the past this had never been made stockproof due to the extreme ruggedness and inaccessibility of the terrain. Nevertheless it was essential to exclude all sheep from the reserve and in an ambitious project in 1992, the RSPB was able to erect a northern march fence. With generous funding from the J. and J.R. Wilson Trust and using the expertise of a local fencing contractor, a new 1300m fence was constructed. The key to this project was using a helicopter to transport fencing material to the very steep hillside (Figure 2). Over seven tons of equipment were dropped on to the site in just two hours, a massive saving in labour and effort. For the first time for about 150 years, Inversnaid is now a sheep free zone. Together with the reduction in deer and goat numbers, grazing pressure in the woods is also on the decline. As a result, the woodland should both thrive and increase its coverage, thus ensuring that the rich natural history of the area will be conserved for future generations to enjoy. The fauna and flora can happily co-exist, providing a compromise is reached between grazing and regeneration rates.

This reduction in grazing levels is very much a long term management policy and it will be many years before the benefits are apparent. In the short term, though, there are other on-going projects to help the woodland. One of these involves the protection of individual naturally regenerating trees on the woodland edge and open moorland using plastic tree shelters. These are put on seedlings at a very early stage to prevent the deer and goats from eating them. It is a constant job to replace these tubes because they are continually battered by the wind and animals, but eventually the tree inside will develop into a mature specimen. Then as the grazing pressure is reduced in the immediate vicinity, these trees will be able to successfully seed on to the adjacent ground and thus extend the woodland.

Likewise, tiny areas of remnant scrub on the moorland are being protected and fenced off, each plot being no more than 150 square metres. Again, this will ensure the future survival of the woodland and protect these remnants before they are finally lost. However, neither of these projects are the final solution of the grazing problem. They will only protect a few isolated trees and shrubs in a very artificial manner. In the short term, though, they will provide a valuable seed source for future natural regeneration to occur.

The existing woodland is an important habitat for a wide range of birds and plants. Every year about 45 bird species breed on the reserve, of which 32 are directly associated with the woodland. Of particular note are those scarce birds which visit us each summer and spend the winter around the Mediterranean or in Africa. One of the Inversnaid specialities is the pied flycatcher, a bird that only breeds irregularly in most parts of Scotland. There are perhaps some 400 pairs in the country, with an important concentration on Loch Lomondside. When the Society originally acquired Inversnaid in 1986 there were just 11 pairs of breeding pied flycatchers, but with the provision of suitable nestboxes, the population of this attractive bird increased to 53 pairs by 1989. This was very encouraging and was much appreciated by visiting birdwatchers, some of whom come to Inversnaid specially to see this bird. However, towards the end of the summer of 1989, several nestboxes were attacked by an unknown mammalian predator. In some cases the lid of the box was ripped off. Other boxes showed signs of an attack with teeth marks clearly visible on the lids and claw rakings on the side. Scuff marks were also noted where the animal climbed the tree.

The situation deteriorated the following year, when from a total of 56 occupied boxes, 25 were predated and a further 14 were deserted after signs of an attack. Not only were pied flycatchers suffering, but blue tits, great tits, spotted flycatchers and redstarts were also affected. By now the predator had been positively identified from its droppings as a pine marten. During the next two years various attempts were made to prevent pine marten attacks on the boxes, ranging from re-inforcing the lids to suspending some of the nestboxes on lengths of wire. Many boxes were closed down while this work was going on and by 1993 when no suitable alternative had been found, serious consideration was given to removing all the remaining nestboxes. Then in the summer of that year news came in of a completely new type of box that had been used for a number of years at the University Field Station near Rowardennan. Although pine martens have not yet reached this part of Loch Lomondside, these boxes were very successful in deterring other types of predators, particularly great spotted woodpeckers.

The nestboxes in question are made in Germany by a company called Schwegler. They are referred to as "woodcrete" nestboxes and are made of a mixture of pine sawdust, burnt clay and concrete. The finished product is then treated with a coat of non-toxic paint. Such boxes are weather resistant, predator resistant, and, unlike wood, completely rot-proof. The woodcrete material also allows the box to 'breathe', thus controlling ranges in temperature and preventing condensation inside.

In the winter of 1993/4 the RSPB purchased 21 of the woodcrete boxes, assisted by a grant from Central Regional Council. These boxes incorporated a new design with a removable front panel particularly well protected against mammalian predators (Figure 3), just what was needed to deter pine martens (Figure 4). This involves a recessed entrance hole that makes it impossible for a pine marten to put its paw into the hole and pull out the box's contents as happens with standard designs. The following summer 17 of the new nestboxes were occupied by breeding birds (pied flycatchers, blue tits and great tits) and not one of them was predated. By comparison one third of the remaining wooden boxes were ransacked by pine martens. The results in 1995 were very similar, so the following winter all the remaining wooden boxes were replaced with woodcrete ones.

The pine martens meanwhile are still thriving and have adapted their omnivorous diet to other items, notably berries, beetles and small mammals. Unfortunately they are remarkably elusive animals and in the seven years that they have been at Inversnaid, there have been very few sightings. However, it is an animal that we will undoubtedly see and hear more of in the future. Formerly common throughout much of Britain, its range has contracted due to a history of persecution. Prior to 1989, the last dated record for pine martens resident on Loch Lomondside was 1832, when a pair was trapped near Luss (correspondence of John Colquhoun March 5th in the J.A.Harvie-Brown papers). In recent years the pine marten has been slowly expanding its range in Scotland, spreading out from its stronghold in the north of the country. This is probably due to better protection for the animal. Under the Wildlife and

Countryside Act 1981, the pine marten was only partly protected in as much as it could not be killed by certain methods. However, at the first Quinquennial review, the Secretary of State for the Environment accepted recommendations that the pine marten should be fully protected. It is now an offence to kill or injure this animal as well as disturb its breeding site.

In 1991 an exciting new project began at Inversnaid which will benefit not only pine martens but also many other forms of wildlife. This is the establishment of a native Scots pinewood on the reserve. When the Society originally acquire the site, it soon became apparent that the reserve did not have any Scots pine, a species that was once common in the area. At the same time it was very obvious that the native pinewood at Glen Falloch, just seven miles north of Inversnaid, was in serious danger of dying out completely. This is the most southerly remnant of the great wood of Caledon that once covered much of Scotland. However, for many years no natural regeneration has taken place due to severe grazing and by 1987 there were just 133 mature trees left. Six years later in 1993 this had been reduced to 115. So it was decided to create a new pinewood at Inversnaid using seed collected from Glen Falloch. At the same time it would be possible to preserve the unique genetic strain found there.

This project was discussed with Scottish Natural Heritage, the Forestry Commission and the factor of the estate. All parties supported the RSPB's proposals, with SNH giving consent to collect pine cones from the site, which is a Site of Special Scientific Interest, and the Commission accepting the project for grant aid under the Woodland Grant Scheme administered by the Forestry Authority.

Work began in 1991 when the first pine cones were collected from Glen Falloch. In the autumn of 1994 a 24ha site of barren moorland on the reserve was deer fenced by contractors. The line of the fence was very carefully planned to take into account the local geomorphology of the site and to be as inconspicuous as possible. Once again all the materials were flown in by helicopter. Tree planting commenced in the spring of 1995 and will continue until well into the next century. Spacing of the trees is varied and reflects geomorphological features of the site. Thus rocky outcrops and boggy hollows are avoided, while some dense thickets are being created. Together with 20% open space within the site, it is hoped that the woodland will look as natural as possible. Existing natural regeneration of other tree species such as birch, willow and hawthorn which until the deer fence was erected never developed into mature specimens, is already beginning to become established. The end result in a hundred years' time will be a pine dominated mixed coniferous/deciduous woodland (Figure 5). This will provide an important wildlife habitat for many forms of wildlife as well as enhance the barren landscape of the area. Specialised Caledonian pinewood birds like capercaillie and crested tit may well colonise the area, the local black grouse population will certainly benefit and the pine martens will also be better off. Eventually it is hoped that the pinewood will be self-sustaining and slowly increase in size as it regenerates naturally on the moorland outside the deer fence. This will correspond with low grazing pressure on the surrounding land, brought about by the careful management of the deer and feral goat populations.

When the RSPB purchased the nature reserve, the only access for visitors to the site was the West Highland Way, along the shore of Loch Lomond. One of the Society's first policies, therefore, was to open up part of the reserve to visitors through the provision of a nature trail. This project in fact did not start until spring 1990 and it was nearly another two years before it was completed. Work was held up in summer by the midges, which make life quite unbearable, and in the winter everything is weather dependent.

The project was very labour intensive. Initially the 800m route had to be dug out by hand, then 432 steps were constructed on the steeper sections. Stone pitching was laid on two damp sections, geotextiles were used on one particularly wet peat bog, drainage ditches were dug and a substantial footbridge was built. Finally the entire path was gravelled over to provide a firm, dry surface to walk on. All this hard graft was carried out by a number of different people - a three man Employment Training workforce did the bulk of the spadework, a five person Pathcraft Ltd squad was responsible for all the difficult sections that required professional expertise, volunteers helped with the steps and gravelling, while RSPB personnel did a bit of everything. A total of 234 man days were spent on the project and the former Countryside Commission for Scotland, now Scottish Natural Heritage, funded half the costs.

Work finished at the beginning of 1992 and later on that year the path was officially opened by Jimmie Macgregor. Since then the nature trail has been enjoyed by many thousands of people, so why not take a run out to Inversnaid to see it for yourself? The path provides a very pleasant walk through the Loch Lomond woods and leads up to a viewpoint just above the trees, providing a spectacular panorama of the loch and surrounding mountains. To reach the trail, follow the West Highland Way northwards from the large public car park by the Inversnaid Hotel. After some 600m the trail branches off to the right, just past the boathouse. It is well signposted, so there is no chance of taking the wrong route. The trail then meanders across the hillside before rejoining the West Highland Way near Rob Roy's Cave, providing a circular walk of about one kilometre in length. Because of the steep terrain involved, there are many steps to negotiate, but four strategically placed benches provide everyone with a resting place en route. The trail is open every day throughout the year and there is no admission charge.

In conjunction with the trail, the RSPB has produced a small guide which contains a map of the route and describes some of the wildlife to look out for. This costs 15p and can be purchased from a dispenser by the car park, at the Inversnaid Hotel and at local Tourist Information Centres. The best time of the year to visit the reserve is in May, when the summer migrants have all just arrived, the bluebells, primroses and other woodland flora are at their best and the midges have not appeared. But at any time of the year there is always something to see, even if it is nothing more than the spectacular views.

A great deal has happened at Inversnaid during the last ten years. There have been a number of exciting developments and the future of the rich woodland habitat now seems assured. The RSPB has also been fortunate to receive funding from other organisations and charities. In addition to those already mentioned, the Society would like to acknowledge generous financial assistance from the Gillman Trust, the World Wide Fund for Nature and the Forestry Commission. Recognition of all the hard work done over the past ten years has also been marked by the winning of a prestigious award. In 1995 the Society was highly commended by the Royal Highland and Agricultural Society of Scotland in their annual Woodland and Forestry awards. The next ten years will not see so much activity on the reserve. It will be a period of consolidation rather than development, but in the long term with the establishment of a native pinewood at Inversnaid, there is still a great deal to look forward to.

Figure 1 Feral Goats grazing in the woodland.

Figure 2: Mike Trubridge loading fencing materials on to helicopter.

Figure 5 Planting Scots pine, March 1996.

Figure 4 Pine Marten at birdbox.
(D. MacCaskill)

Figure 3 Woodcrete nestbox.

WILDLIFE CONSERVATION COMES TO GRANGEMOUTH – THE JUPITER PROJECT

William R. Brackenridge

The Jupiter Project is one of the most unusual - some would say, improbable - initiatives to provide nature conservation and environmental education in the whole of Scotland. It is essentially a partnership between the **Scottish Wildlife Trust** (SWT), (itself the Scottish wing of the Royal Society for Nature Conservation's Wildlife Trusts' Partnership) and **Zeneca**, the pharmaceuticals, dyestuffs, agricultural and horticultural chemicals division of the former ICI conglomerate.

It all started back in 1989, when a senior staff member of the ICI Grangemouth Works, then under pressure to 'clean up its act' by Greenpeace and others, visited a Scottish Wildlife Trust exhibit in Stirling. Original ideas included funding a bird hide, planting a pipeline track and developing a small patch of the firm's traditionally-landscaped recreation ground on the west side of the factory. However, these quickly gave way when mention was made of a long derelict strip of land to the east of the factory. This had been planned as the 'Em Nine' industrial estate by the Central Regional Council but proved to be unsuitable. Its condition had become a subject of complaints from the adjacent housing and community leaders. So the idea of Scotland's **biggest** showpiece wildlife garden was born, appropriate for a multinational company developing a worldwide 'Nature Link' scheme. Indeed some of the original funding came out of this initiative–

The aims of the original project, as agreed by SWT and ICI environmental management were –
1. *to foster an increasing sensitivity towards wildlife, using a hands-on approach;*
2. *to provide training opportunities in wildlife conservation skills and to promote their wider use;*
3. *to promote an interest in and awareness of science and technology;*
4. *to to provide a resource which will aid and encourage a greater understanding of wider environmental issues.*

The joint SWT-ICI (Zeneca) steering group then set about planning the transformation of the site to accommodate the garden, associated nursery, and the Urban Wildlife Centre which developed during 1991.

Integral to the project is the management of an introductory 'formal' wildflower garden with laid out paths and familiar features. Beyond this a very large (2 hectare) wildlife garden was landscaped around two large ponds, the excavated material forming grassy hillocks with over 1000 planted trees and shrubs surrounding the various created habitat features. The overall layout was designed by Christopher Palmer, a Glasgow-based landscape architect. Beyond a dividing fence lies a fascinating adjacent area of semi-natural regeneration - grass, reeds, bramble, willow and birches, appropriately termed 'the Wilderness'. All this, measuring about 450 metres long, 85 metres wide was part of former railway marshalling yards within 200 metres of the chemical factory.

It is relevant to note that ICI acquired this land in the mid 1980's, to act as a 'cordon sanitaire' due to health and safety issues arising from the potentially hazardous nature of operations and chemical substances used by the works. This affects the numbers of visitors allowed to visit the site and certain safety procedures have to be followed to comply with Health and Safety regulations.

Jupiter's wealth of wildlife

Surveys of the existing site's botany and entomology carried out in 1990 by SWT experts soon revealed that it had considerable existing biodiversity, with around 200 vascular plants esablished on the slag-type surface which had been laid down when the sidings were built - the original site had been marshy (hence the local name Fouldubs) and several patches of reed *Phragmites communis* still occur. Of particular interest was a colony of a tall sedge (*Carex* sp.) not known from anywhere else in the region and possibly established from a seed brought in (via neighbouring timber yards) from Scandinavia or beyond. Other unusual species in certain parts of the planned garden and wilderness, also in an 'unofficial nature reserve' area behind the Centre, include the following species. Some of the plants are new to the Falkirk District checklist (Stewart 1988) and all are nowadays scarce in central Scotland.

Plants

Common Broomrape	*Orobanche minor* (the only site in central Scotland)
Common Centaury	*Centaurium erythraea*
Kidney Vetch	*Anthyllis vulneraria*
Bladder Campion	*Silene vulgaris*
Smooth Tare	*Vicia tetrasperma*
Common Birdsfoot	*Ornithopus perpusillus*
Bush-grass	*Calamagrostis epigejos*

The wilderness area also includes some handsome specimens of the hybrid Marsh Orchid (*Orchis purpurella* x *O. fuchsii*) as well as a wealth of other commoner species. The clash of colour amongst the Red Clover *Trifolium pratense*, Meadow Pea *Lathyrus pratensis*, Tufted Vetch *Vicia cracca* and Ox-eye Daisies *Leucanthemum vulgare* is a delight to the eye in June and July.

Invertebrates

For such an urban -indeed industrial- location, the list of insects and other invertebrates is already impressive and growing. The following are of note:

Six-spotted Burnet	*Zygaena filipendulae* (over 230 counted in July 1992)
Hornet Clearwing	*Sesia bembeciformis*
Elephant Hawk-moth	*Deilephila elpenor*
Common Blue	*Polyommatus icarus*

In 1991 the site was visited by three Clouded Yellow butterflies *Colias crocea*, and Red Admirals *Vanessa atalanta* and Painted Ladies *V. cardui* are more regular visitors, supplementing the resident Small Tortoiseshell *Aglais urticae* and Meadow Brown *Maniola jurtina*. A variety of other moths, ichneumon wasps, honey and bumble bees, grasshoppers (including a particularly attractive crimson and emerald variety of the Meadow Grasshopper *Chorthippus* sp., beetles and spiders have also been identified. Since the ponds were dug into the carse clays, countless sticklebacks, several species of damselfly, two dragonflies, water beetles, boatmen and skaters, even water scorpions have turned up, whilst frogspawn was successfully introduced by a factory employee in 1992, leading to frogs being a regular sight in spring.

Birds and Mammals

The wide range of birds found in the site includes breeding Song Thrush, Dunnock, Willow Warbler, Reed Bunting, Sedge Warbler, Whitethroat and - more surprisingly, perhaps - Grey Partridge. Lesser Black-backed Gulls nest on the roof of the centre and Swallows nested inside the warehouse in 1993. In winter, Blue and Long-tailed Tits are frequent and Goldfinches, and Grey and Pied Wagtails visit form time to time. One of a pair of Kestrels is often seen, though unfortunately these prefer the factory buildings to the specially-provided nestbox on a pole installed by BT. A Sparrowhawk hunts along the entrance road. Since the main pond was created, it has attracted Common Sandpiper, Mute Swan, Mallard, nesting Moorhen and Coot, and even Red-breasted Merganser has been observed.

As for mammals, apart from the feral cats, fed by some neighbouring householders in Wood Street, nocturnal Grangemouth foxes, which feed on the abundant wood mice and field voles, appear from time to time. A weasel was seen in 1992, a water vole (a nationally-declining species) turned up in 1995, and very recently a roe deer somehow negotiated the security fence (and the M9 motorway) to get into the wilderness.

The Urban Wildlife Centre

For an agreed sum provided annually by ICI (from 1992, Zeneca), SWT has developed and promoted this Centre within part of a large warehouse formerly occupied by a DIY outlet called 'Jupiter'. The original Urban Wildlife Ranger, Bill Brackenridge, was appointed in July 1991 on a three year contract, to oversee the main development phase of both the centre and the wildlife garden. This proved to be a mammoth task, but much assistance was offered by John Hendry from ICI (then Engineering Planner), and several others from the works helped, in spite of the 'downsizing' of the workforce which had limited the volunteer effort from the factory previously anticipated.

In accordance with the project aims, the Centre has been used for the study and practice of wildlife conservation in the urban context. Since the centre was officially opened by Magnus Magnusson in April 1992, it has developed as a Scottish focus for training events, and has become the base for the SWT's Forth Valley Conservation team, funded by recent Government schemes for unemployed people.

The Centre has audio-visual facilities, an extensive library, exhibition space (which has been used for the first ever Scottish Wildflower Show!), tools and equipment stores. It hosts meetings of the Scottish Urban Wildlife Partnership, now only one of a wide network of urban conservation groups throughout the UK, and school group visits (within the operational constraints of the factory). It also provides project facilities for college or university student placements. Most importantly, the Urban Wildlife Ranger, and Nursery Manager are there to assist in the 'hands-on' experience for local volunteers who are interested in wildflowers and other native plants; and their vital role in providing food and shelter for all our wildlife, as well as their uses, past and present, to people.

Creating the garden flora

In January 1992, the landscaping team from Training Craft Limited, supervised by Owen Bass and creators of the formal garden layout, had an additional task, in translocating around fifty trees and shrubs from a site on the other side of the factory which has now become Zeneca's integrated effluent treatment plant. Amazingly most of these, including large hawthorns, elders, birch, oak, ash and a wych elm survived their upheaval and journey by lorry and digger. The ten birches made the nucleus of the 'birch copse' and the elm (now a rare species, thanks to the elm disease) graces a corner of the formal garden.

Smaller-scale "plant rescues" were undertaken within the site, from areas where the landscaping was inevitable; among those translocated on site, the Kidney Vetch survived better than the Centaury, whilst the Hard Rush *Juncus inflexus* has taken well around the ponds. In addition, a number of other aquatic and meadow species came from the Union Canal near Linlithgow, a threatened site in Stirling brought Water Figwort *Scrophularia auriculata*, and from a field at Polmont, now a housing development, came orchids dug up respectively by local Sea Scouts, Venture Scouts and Girls' Brigade members.

Imported plants have arrived on the site ever since 1991, including various personal gifts (e.g. Spindle Tree seeds), young trees and 'garden extras' from ICI/Zeneca workers and SWT members. However the main diversification took place in the formal garden during 1992, using coir-grown young plants from a specialist supplier (Martin Gould, Stockerton Nursery, Kirkcudbright). The bulk of the trees - apart from those rescued and the oak requested by Magnus Magnusson - were obtained from Bellwood Nurseries and Scottish Landscaping. The combination of all these efforts has raised the total plant list to almost 400, most of them now established somewhere on the site.

The wildflower nursery, based in the polytunnels has been developed since Campbell Ferguson took over as the site ranger in August 1994. This is being developed as a new outlet for Scottish-grown seeds and plants to supply the steadily-growing interest in wildflower sales. To establish more interest, the first ever Wildflower Show was held in the centre in 1993; then a Fun Day, with wider environmental messages was launched in 1994, whilst the site has taken part in the BTO/Zeneca Bird Challenge, an inventory of birds observed on industrial sites nationwide.

Education, in the form of school visits, originally given travel incentives in Central Region, placement students, youth groups and indeed SWT and similar adult organisations, continues to be a main function of the site. Visitors can view the development phase on the video featuring Mike Scott or request a guided tour.

Any group or individual wishing to learn more about, visit or indeed participate in this amazing venture, is requested to contact the Urban Wildlife Ranger at Jupiter Urban Wildlife Centre, Wood Street, Grangemouth FK3 8LH. Telephone (01324) 494974.

Reference

Stewart, N. F. A. 1988. Checklist of the Vascular Plants of Falkirk District, *Forth Naturalist and Historian*, 10, 53-79.

Update by Campbell Ferguson (Ranger 1994-September 1996)

In 1994 Jupiter was awarded an Environmental Regeneration Award by Scottish Natural Heritage and Scottish Enterprise, and in the following year became the first (and only to date!) site in Scotland to be included in the Man and Biosphere Programme – a European designation, organised under the auspices of UNESCO. It means Jupiter is on a list of recommended premier urban nature conservation sites in the UK.

Additional wildlife sightings since Brackenridge include – several butterflies, making 11 species; four species of dragonfly; and toads and newts breeding in the ponds. For birds we have Linnet and Meadow Pipit, Bullfinch and Mallards nesting. Of fauna we have stoats and weasels as regular visitors and the occasional mink.

Kate Bovill has been fulfilling the role of Nursery Manager since September 1995 and the new Ranger is Helen Sadler.

Young volunteers, formal garden, July 1992.

JUPITER WILDLIFE CENTRE

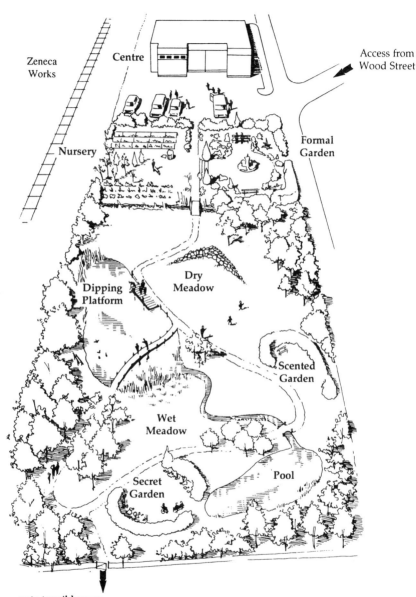

Zeneca Works

Centre

Access from Wood Street

Nursery

Formal Garden

Dipping Platform

Dry Meadow

Scented Garden

Wet Meadow

Secret Garden

Pool

gate to wilderness and hide

THE HEART OF SCOTLAND'S ENVIRONMENT (HSE) –
An Environmental Database on CD-ROM

David Grinly

BACKGROUND TO PROJECT

The range of environmental issues and problems across the region made this an ideal subject for an Environmental Education project. Central Regional Council made a commitment towards improving its environmental performance in its manifesto in 1990. *The Environmental Charter* recognised the need for "environmental education to be more coherently structured and available to pupils at all stages, on a cross curricular basis ... to provide all pupils with knowledge and understanding of the main environmental issues."

Through the appointment of an Environmental Education Development Officer the Council promoted these ideas; but the multi-media project met a specific *Charter* objective, namely that.. "The Council should improve the quality of education on the environment that it provides, not only in schools, but to the whole community," – hence a point in the Action Programme ... "produce a multi-media computer based environmental information package by August 1994."

The first CD produced was a pilot – PHASE ONE of the project. Initially this was to follow two of the topic headings all the way through to a level usable by upper secondary pupils. In the event an attempt was made to include information up to this depth of understanding for all 10 topics – Landscape; Climate; Vegetation; Wildlife; Built Environment; People, Health and Welfare; Industry and Economy; Pollution and Resource Conservation; Transport; Recreation, Leisure and Tourism.

Early work on the project centred on the design of the database – how the material was to be presented – how were users to access the information? Several other databases were examined, with *Europe in the Round* looking an attractive way of moving around information about the twelve member states, chopped into categories common to each country. This allowed the user to jump from one piece of information to another much more readily than was possible when dealing with 10 discrete subject areas.

Initial ideas about moving from one topic to another via a suite of maps proved more difficult to implement than at first thought. There were no such maps. Co-operation was forthcoming from other services within Central Regional Council. Particularly helpful were Development & Planning who had much environmental data and expertise at their disposal.

Phase 1 CD had a short introduction available in English, German and French and a help sequence to set the scene and to introduce the ten subject or topic areas mentioned above. The user could then opt to hear and view a 'tape/slide' presentation on any or all of the 10 topics or go straight to more in-depth text than in the tape/slide commentary, and/or graphs, statistics, photographs, moving image – depending on topic chosen. Quit buttons allowed the user to return to the main menu at any time.

This Phase 1 CD was launched in late 1994. It operated on the Acorn / Archimedes platform as this type of computer was the local authority norm. Problems arising from this choice of platform however included the paucity of machines powerful enough to run the CD and the low resolution graphics inherent in writing to a fairly low level of minimum requirement. The authoring package first chosen was supposedly a cross platform one enabling Archimedes and PC discs to be produced – however two weeks before the deadline for completing the CD it was found to be non-compatible, so no PC version was possible.

The Regional Council's European Office in conjunction with the Multi-Media Environmental Education Project Officers – (Alan Speedie, Central Region's Environment Officer and myself) lodged a bid with the Commission of the European Communities for financial support for Phase 2 of the project, under call 94/C 68/13 – "Projects in the area of Environmental Education." This bid was unsuccessful and the chance to gather environmental information from other EU member state schools was lost.

In late 1994 work on Phase 2 began. I was appointed Project Manager and awarded a commission to compile the information for the database. Two important decisions were made early on, namely:–

the platform would be PC, since secondary schools were equipped with this type of computer, as were the then District libraries and other associated departments. The reason for this restriction was that Phase 2 was to include Ordnance Survey data. OS are extremely strict about copyright and the Service Level Agreement between OS and the local authority means that use is restricted to establishments wholly or partly funded by the authority. Had we charged for each CD, then OS would have required a heftier fee for use of the data as we would have been regarded as making a profit from their copyright material. The same restrictions applied to satellite data – if we made a profit from use of the material then the agents from whom we obtained the images would have required a higher fee. For copyright reasons no satellite images or OS data should be printed from the database.

the database would be programed professionally by SCET – the Scottish Council for Educational Technology. The authoring software to be used was 'Toolbook', which allowed the production of a CD on PC platform only.

COMPONENT PARTS OF THE DATABASE

Photographs

Sourcing photographs was found to be a major headache. Time and financial constraints meant that printing from negatives held in photo archives was not an option. In Phase 2 the transparency images were scanned by a company in Glasgow and put onto Photo CD and we were fortunately put in touch with two sources of wildlife photographs – Mr Doig from Dunning and Mr Smith from Bo'ness. Earlier I had taken it upon myself to make line drawings of all 120 bird species and many of the mammals found in the region in case we drew a blank in our search for these images. As for other images in the database, the bulk of them were taken specifically to match the commentary within the 'Slide show' sections.

Satellite images

After lengthy negotiations with a number of companies, the project settled on photographs of the area from April 17 1987 – an almost cloudless run of three satellite photographs which have been colour enhanced. The images can be zoomed in twice to give a fairly reasonable image at good resolution.

Maps

Liaison with the GIS (Geographical Information Systems) Department of Central Region meant that we had access to a huge body of data. In a complex procedure enormous amounts were downloaded from the GIS computers into Development and Planning's PCs – each large 1:50,000 raster file taking around 45 minutes to transfer. From the large volume of data available we settled for the whole region at 1:50,000 scale and selected areas at 1:10,000. The 1:10,000 data on computer lacks contours so there was little point in including areas of impressive scenery!

Other maps included those from the Forth Naturalist and Historian publication *Central Scotland – land, wildlife, people*, and other Central Region publications. Colour imaging of some, particularly Geology was achieved by Alistair Ogilvie and the Development and Planning computers.

Sound

Commentaries by Karen Clark of B.B.C. Radio Scotland were recorded in Central FM studios in Stirling. In Phase 1 individual topic commentaries were lengthy but in Phase 2 they were made much shorter and designed so that they could be interrupted. This involved much rearranging of text and audio files plus background work on screen design, as some topics like 'Industry and Economy' now had as many as seven sub-topics, each with its own slide show.

Text

The text in HSE came from a number of sources. The bulk being from *Central Scotland – land, wildlife, people* published by The Forth Naturalist and Historian. In order to be more accessible the individual chapters were split up to allow the user to identify a particular section for study – again this meant further menus, sub-menus and linkages within the branching format of the database.

Other sources were *Central 2000* – Central Region's Structure Plan and *All*

Change – the authority's transport policy document. Other material came from publications of the Scottish Tourist Board, HMSO, and environmental audits from Falkirk, Lancashire and Humberside. Much material was written specifically for the database – e.g. the commentaries which accompany the slide shows. In all there are over 520 text files.

Hardware

The major user purchase required apart from a computer is a large hard disc drive to hold and allow sorting of the information. As a CD holds around 660 Mb of information the bigger the hard drive the better.

Time

The most time demanding aspects of the project included – sourcing photographs, or failing that to take appropriate images, select the best, arrange for scanning; arranging text files, subdividing them into reasonable sizes, typing up menus to show what files are available, whether they be text, figures, tables, maps; arranging scanning of other graphic material; matching images to commentary; identifying files where an appropriate map might be made available; identifying files where a 'hot link' would allow the user to jump from one file within a topic to a related file within another.

Such was merely the beginning. To facilitate SCET's task of putting together all this material it was necessary to 'map out' exactly where each file fitted into the overview of the database. What this meant in practice was allotting a place for each of more than 520 text files and over 220 graphics. The only way that this could be done was to design the database before it went to SCET and provide them with a 'map' of where every file fitted in. The cost of asking SCET to do it would have been in the order of four times what was spent on producing *Heart of Scotland's Environment*. Thus I embarked on a task which was to take months. The opening sequence had to be mapped out, allowing 15 different choices to the user and it was necessary to build in a 'HELP' system – text files to explain what each button would do when clicked. This meant mapping out where the 'speech bubbles' should appear – again each of these screen variations had to be illustrated by means of a post card.

Eventually the data was in place and sent to SCET in Glasgow. The problems then became long distance – e.g. altered names of files, misorientation of photographs and much more.

Once the database appeared on screen other problems arose, e.g. the colour of backgrounds, size and colour of text, size and position of buttons and so on.

The CD did eventually go to press and finally was launched on Tuesday 21st May 1996, accompanied by a *User's Guide* which explained installation and use, listed the text files and maps available, and mapped out the areas of the curriculum served by the database.

Postscript

For anyone contemplating producing a CD I quote from John Davitt's 'DIY

Megastores', *Times Educational Supplement* 26th March 1993 ..."it is easy to underestimate the time needed to design, gather and edit the material to fill a standard CD-ROM disc". In real terms it took fully two years to put together *Heart of Scotland's Environment* – the bulk of that work being outwith the time allowed for information gathering. In fact as the previous paragraphs show, gathering the material is only the beginning.

From the outset the project was double-edged – the fillip of being involved in the exploration of uncharted territory (no local authority in the UK had attempted a project of this magnitude) was countered by the thought that we were wandering into technological areas where no-one had yet set foot! In conclusion, despite all the long hours working on the database, seeing the project through to its conclusion was immensely rewarding, enjoyable and satisfying.

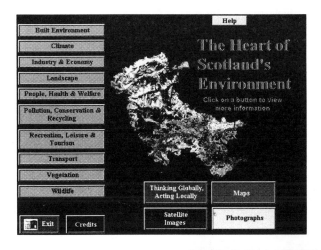

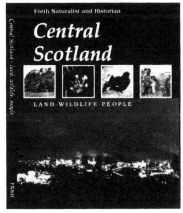

BOOK REVIEWS AND NOTES (Historical)

Falkirk or Paradise! The Battle of Falkirk Muir, 17 January 1746. Geoff B. Bailey. John Donald. 250pp. ISBN 0.85976.431.1. £9.95.

Meticulously researched, including contemporary eye witness accounts, and involvements of neighbouring places – Airth, Bo'ness, Alloa – this work details some ten days sojourn of the victorious Highlanders around Falkirk. It focusses on the build up to, then the resulting devastating blow to the Hanovarian army. Here was the largest battle of the '45 Rising with over 18,000 combatants on the field and the Jacobite army at full strength returning from its invasion of England. As local history this is a companion to Ian Scott's *Life and Times of Falkirk*, also by John Donald. Assuredly distinguished and "memorable local history" as claimed by the publisher, though less surely perhaps "of great popular appeal".

The Carron Company ... in the Beginning; and **Waterpower:** two papers by Brian Watters in *Calatria* (Jnl. of the Falkirk Local History Society), no.9 Summer 1996. pp67-84.

Expertly presented from first sources.

The Battle of Stirling Bridge.

1997 is the 700th anniversary, and the battle and the bridge are objects of much celebration and interest, spurred by the Braveheart film and various books and exhibitions on Wallace, including that at the Smith Art Gallery and Museum in Stirling. In 1984 our late FNH Board member David Angus aired his views on the preparations leading up to the battle (briefly reported in *CFSS Newsletter* 32, 27-9), and in 1994 in FNH 17, 103-110 we published Ron Page's 'The Ancient Bridge of Stirling: a new survey' which discusses its history and studies and surveys of it. It was anticipated that a follow-up sonar survey on 25th September 1996 might be briefly reported on here, but technical problems of some complexity (including satellite tracking, Geological Survey and the University) have frustrated this interest. The objective was to detect further remains of the ancient bridge, advancing on previous investigations in 1907, 1990 and 1992. A Stirling Ancient Bridge Trust is now in being and it hopes to make an underwater archaeological excavation of two known piers in spring 1997.

LC

PREHISTORIC ROCK ART AROUND CASTLETON FARM, AIRTH, CENTRAL SCOTLAND

M. A. M. van Hoek.
(Paper first submitted 1993)

INTRODUCTION

Neolithic and Early Bronze Age cup-and-ring art is found all over Britain and Ireland. While many rock art sites occur in clusters for reasons as yet unexplained, many sites prove to be situated on possible prehistoric routes, especially in central Scotland with its long glens and lochs providing through-ways. The area can boast of three major groups of rock art: Duncroisk in Glenlochay, Menteith, and Castleton.

As with the article about Menteith (Van Hoek 1991), the discovery of new sites justifies this review of Castleton, especially since one engraved outcrop (No. 6) was for a short time endangered by quarrying – fortunately abandoned because of poor quality of stone (L Main pers. comm. 1995). The fine sites at Castleton Wood (No's 4, 5, 7 and 9) are scheduled as Ancient Monuments and have legal protection (L Main pers. comm. 3/2/92).

SITUATION

The complex at Castleton lies some 8 km SE of Stirling (Figure 1), some 2km inland of the Forth in a low rolling landscape. It is a series of low craggy outcrop ridges with wide views across the Forth Valley towards the Ochil Hills and the mountains of Ben Lomond, Ben Ledi and Ben Venue to the north and west.

The ridges are characterised by steep scarps and more gentle dip-slopes and in most cases the engravings are found close to the escarpments. As the ridges were of little use to the farmers they became overgrown, walled all around, and mostly covered by rough grass, bracken, gorse and some trees. They stretch from NW–SE to NNE–SSW, altitude about 40m OD with some ridges up to 50m.

THE ENGRAVINGS

Altogether 20 decorated surfaces have been examined by the author over the past few years. Three more sites have been reported but could not be traced on several visits. All but three sites have cup-and-ring motifs. Morris (1981, pp 44-50) reported more rocks with cups-only but, except for Castleton 1B and 7D, several searches by the author only yielded natural pittings. All single 'cups', especially when not accompanied with cup-and-rings, must be viewed with suspicion; most will be natural.

Eleven of the carved rocks have been described by Morris (1981) and he

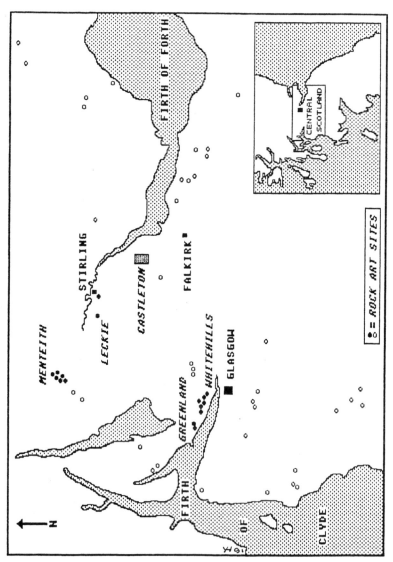

Figure 1. Rock art sites in the central part of Scotland. Solid dots are sites mentioned in the text.

numbered them Castleton 1, 2, 3, 4A, 4B, 4C, 5A, 5B, 5C, 5D and 6. At least two new rocks were discovered by Lorna Main and Gordon Barclay in March 1985, Castleton 7A and 7B, and in May of that year an Ordnance Survey Team discovered Castleton 8. The locations of these were kindly pointed out to me by former landowner Mr Johnston in July 1985, and I then found another, 7C. A year later Mrs Morris discovered Castleton 9. On visiting the latter in July 1986 Mr Morris and the author found two minor sites, 4D and 5E (Morris and Van Hoek, 1986, p 5). In 1989 numbers were allocated for possible sites 10 and 11; but No. 10 was a misunderstood grid reference, and 11 could not be located because of dense vegetation. In August 1991 three other minors, 1B, 2B and 7D were found. Many sites have become overgrown with gorse and by 1991 4A, 4B, 5B, 5C, and 5D were no longer visible. The fine rock at 7A is almost invisible.

The gazetteer below lists 22 sites with descriptions, particularly of new sites and additions and alterations to existing sites. Each entry gives (approximate!) grid reference and altitude, slopes of carved surfaces, and references to illustrations and earlier literature; Morris's book (1981) gives further references. All site-locations are shown on the sketch map of the area which has a 100m grid (Figure 2).

GAZETTEER

CASTLETON 1A. NS 85878840; 45m.

Five finely executed cup and rings; as described and illustrated by Morris, except that they are on a surface sloping 15° to the north (Morris 1981, p 44, Plate 30, Figure 38).

CASTLETON 1B. NS 85898839; 43 m.

On the very SE end of the same ridge on a squarish ledge of rock are two small cupmarks.

CASTLETON 2A and B. NS 85818831; 43m.

Rock (2A) could not be relocated on several visits. It bears a ring mark (no cup) and a (natural?) basin (ibid p 44, Plate 31). In 1991 the author could only find a carved rock very near the probably covered 2A site. This outcrop 2B (Figure 4) shows two roughly cut disc-cups, 10cm apart, with diameters of 13 and 16cm. Their flat bottoms show distinct large pock-marks – of a later date?

CASTLETON 3. NS 85718797; 50m; Figure 4.

On the highest point of the long ridge immediately south of the farm buildings, but north of the Trig. Point (48m) and the Bruce Castle ruin, is this fine group of engravings. It is close to the steep and craggy west face of the ridge and slowly becoming overgrown with gorse. The carvings are as described by Morris except for some details.

There are two engraved surfaces. The north part slopes 9° to the north and has two cups with two rings each. The smaller is clearly unfinished and possibly the pocking of the east part of the outer ring caused a part of the rock to flake off. Undescribed are a very small cup and one complete ring, and a faint cup with incomplete ring in between the two larger devices although Morris (1981 p 47, Plate 34) gives a clear photograph of all these features. The south group is dominated by a large but worn cup-and-five-complete-rings on a surface sloping 16° SSW. It is encircled by four rather distinct cup-and-rings and one very faint cup with one incomplete ring, which has never been reported. All single cups drawn on the plan are very doubtful and probably all are natural, especially the small ones (ibid, Figure 39).

Most important in every respect is the area to the NW of the farm buildings, called Castleton Wood (Figure 3). The wood has now been felled apart from a small coppice in the NW corner. Originally it was planned to quarry this high ridge but because of the importance of the rock art here (fourteen Castleton sites) permission was refused.

CASTLETON 4A. NS 85538816; 52m; Figure 4.

Rock 4A is as described by Morris except that the eastmost cup-and-ring also has a radial groove running ESE from the central cup and there is a single groove in between the two cup-and-rings.

CASTLETON 4B. NS 85538816; 52m.

Two cups with three rings, incomplete in one case.

CASTLETON 4C. NS 85548815; 52m; Figure 4.

One isolated cup with four rings. 4A, B, and C as described by Morris (1981, p 47).

CASTLETON 4D. NS 85548815; 52m; Figure 4.

A small cup-and-one-complete-ring on horizontal outcrop rock as described by Morris and Van Hoek (1986).

CASTLETON 5A. NS 85568812; 50m; Figure 5.

Two cups with four and five rings. In 1991 the author noticed a very faint oval ring with faint central cup and perhaps a cup with almost worn-off single ring, all on the same outcrop on slightly higher levels. The southmost cup is very near the naturally pitted escarpment and therefore is doubtful.

CASTLETON 5B. NS 85568812; 50m.

Two cups with two and three rings.

CASTLETON 5C. NS 85568812; 51m.

One cup-and-one-ring.

CASTLETON 5D. NS 85568813; 51m.

One cup-and-one-ring. 5A, B, C and D as described by Morris (1981, p 50).

CASTLETON 5E. NS 85568813; 51m; Figure 5.

One cup-and-one-ring as described by Morris and Van Hoek (1986).

CASTLETON 6. NS 85988825; 43m; Figure 5.

Morris (p 50, Plates 38–9) reported 9 single cups and one cup-and-one-ring. In 1991 only 5 certain cups were visible. The eastmost cup is deep and conical though of a normal diameter. The cup-and-one-ring proved to be very near the heavily pitted edge of the rock which makes its nature rather doubtful. There possibly is another faint cup surrounded by an irregular horse-shoe ring.

CASTLETON 7A. NS 85518818; 51m; Figure. 6. Plate 1.

The most important set of motifs in the whole area is found at Castleton Wood on a smooth outcrop sloping up to 13° NNE. Some motifs are extremely faint while others are still very clear. Dominating this group is a very large cup-and-nine-complete-rings (70cm) with seven radial grooves, all stopping at the outer ring except for a forked groove. This rock and all others at Castleton Wood are fortunately scheduled as Ancient Monuments.

CASTLETON 7B. NS 85518818; 50m; Figure 6.

Only four metres further northwest and near an isolated birch-tree is a small outcrop slab sloping 2° NNW bearing five much worn cup-and-rings and one certain cupmark.

CASTLETON 7C. NS 85518819; 49m; Figure 6.

Some eleven metres further north and at a lower level is a small outcrop ridge south of a small coppice of birch trees. Deturfing part of this ridge revealed a fine cup with three rings with a broadly pocked tail; one solo cup; one large oval ring with small central cup; and a faint cup with two rings, the outer one incomplete. The rock slopes 12° NE.

CASTLETON 7D. NS 85518819; 49m.

Small outcrop with one cupmark some 13m NW of rock 7B.

CASTLETON 8. NS 8602 8772; 45m; Figure 7.

At the SW end of a high rocky ridge in a walled coppice is a very extensive outcrop, much scarred and pitted by erosion. Near the edge are five cup-and-rings and possibly up to four single cups, all on rock sloping about 6° to 12° NNW. The eastmost set consists of the worn remains of three rings (the innermost hardly visible) without a distinct central cup. Across a crack is a cup with four rings, the outer incomplete and curving away; another cup with four rings, mostly incomplete. A small cup-and-one-ring sits in between. South of this group may be some grooves and a single cup, all doubtful being very near the cliff-edge which is heavily pitted by erosion. The westmost cup with three ovalish rings is the best preserved set of the group. Further away from the scarp is one single cup on a horizontal part and even further N is a cup-and-two-rings on a part sloping 6° SW.

CASTLETON 9. NS 85518826; 43m; Figure 7.

Discovered by Mrs Margaret Morris in 1986 in the birch-coppice at Castleton Wood. A fragment of outcrop rock with a distinct cup-and-three-rings, rather oval shaped like others in the area (eg at 7A and 8).

CASTLETON 10. There is in fact no Castleton 10. This originated from a faulty grid reference giving a location just east of the ruins of Bruce's Castle, but no carvings are traceable anywhere around the castle.

CASTLETON 11. NS 86158771; 35m.

Lorna Main informed the author in 1989 of a cup-and-ring site just north of Avenue Plantation where many outcrops exist. It was found by the Royal Commission in 1985. The engravings comprise "one cup with one penanular ring and possibly a second cup with one ring. There were other traces of heavily weathered engravings". No carvings could be traced in 1990/91 because of the dense vegetation.

DISCUSSION

Castleton is undoubtedly one of the most important groups of rock art sites in this Forth Valley which provided an easy east–west route through Scotland. Some minor sites, such as King's Park, Stirling and Leckie, Gargunnock link Castleton with the major concentration of rock art like Whitehills and Greenland, just NW of Glasgow (Figure 1). The fact that both these rock art groups are situated on either end of this west–east route opens the possibility of Castleton being a point of assembly or even the major (ceremonial?) centre at the east end of the route which may explain the high concentration of decorated rocks there.

The cup and ring art at Castleton is special in many respects: e.g. it is striking that there are no gapped rings: the way the rings have been executed is quite uniform (except perhaps at Castleton 6): rings are well balanced and rather delicately pocked out: most rings are perfectly circular but a number are deliberately laid out elliptically. Also remarkable is the almost complete absence of tailed figures. Only three devices have tails or radial grooves (4A, 7A and 7C) which is only 5% of the total of cup and rings at Castleton compared with 70% at Achnabreck 1, Argyll. There are also very few single cups; only 21 compared with more than a 100 at Achnabreck 1.

There have been counted some 67 or 69 cup and rings. Normally the number of motifs decreases when the number of rings per motif increases: so in general cups with one ring are most common. At Castleton however this is not the case as cups with three rings each predominate: 23 examples, which is 36%.

Castleton has also gained importance through the discovery of the fine cup-and-nine rings on rock 7A. As far as I am aware this is the sixth example to be found in Britain. The other eight known cup-and-nine-rings, in Britain plus Ireland, are:

Bombie 3A;*	outcrop; (covered); Galloway; NX 72534984.
Balcraig 1A;	outcrop; (covered); Galloway; NX 37764438.
Greenland 1D;	outcrop; (removed); Dunbartonshire; NS 434746.
Knockmany 2;	chambered tomb; Co. Tyrone; H 555558.
Loughcrew L19;	chambered tomb; Co. Meath; N 570770.
Torrs 4;**	outcrop; Galloway; NX 68074519.
Townhead 13;***	outcrop; (covered); Galloway; NX 69864685.
Youghal;	Co. Cork, now in the National Museum, Dublin.

*/*** Discovered by A. Miller, L. Lees, J. Tindal, K. Naddair and R. Baldock in 1989; *** Incorrectly reported as Milton 20.
**   Discovered by the author in October 1992 (Van Hoek 1993, Figure 5).
All Galloway sites are described in Van Hoek (1995).

Plate 1. Castleton 7A, looking SW.

In this context mention must be made of a cup with ten concentric rings on an outcrop at Ballyculter, Co. Down (Grid ref J 5712 4725), and of the enormous set of possibly seventeen rings around a cup at Monte Teton 1, Galicia, Spain. At Castleton, ten of the twenty surveyed engraved rock panels slope 10° or more. Only five are horizontal. There is also no clear preference of surfaces sloping in a specific compass-direction. Only the east and south east facing surfaces do not have engravings, a matter most likely to be determined by the natural dip-slope direction of the rock formations.

As Castleton is a very important rock art group the author would favour a full excavation of all sites and a careful preservation afterwards. At least the main sites should not be left open to weathering. He moreover strongly recommends that quarrying should be refused at the remaining sites.

ACKNOWLEDGEMENTS

I would like to thank Mr and Mrs Jarvie, owners since 1988 and Mr Johnston, the former landowner, for access to their land. Mr Johnston kindly directed me to some of the new sites and also provided some information used in this paper.

I am indebted to Ronald Morris for permission to use information from his book (1981) and for informing me of the new site at Castleton 9. Also to Lorna Main, Archaeology Officer of Central Regional Council, for supplying updated information.

LITERATURE

Van Hoek 1991. A survey of the prehistoric rock art of the Port of Menteith Parish, Central Scotland. *Forth Naturalist and Historian*, 15, 58–75.
Van Hoek 1993. *Discovery and Excavation in Scotland*, 24, Figure 5.
Van Hoek 1995. Morris Prehistoric Rock Art of Galloway. Priv. print Van Hoek, Oisterwijk, Holland (copy at RCAHMS, Edinburgh).
Morris, R. W. B. 1981. The Prehistoric Rock Art of Southern Scotland. BAR British Series 86, Oxford.
Morris, R and Van Hoek, M. 1986. Notes in *Discovery and Excavation in Scotland*, 1986, page 5.

CORRIGENDA for the Menteith paper in Volume 15.
p 58, Figure 2   :   No. 12 should read No. 26.
p 69, Figure 8B   :   is inverted.
p 70, at No. 16   :   30° should read 7°.
p 70, at No. 17   :   40° should read 3°.
p 73, Figure 12   :   is inverted.
p 74, at No. 32   :   20° should read 2°.

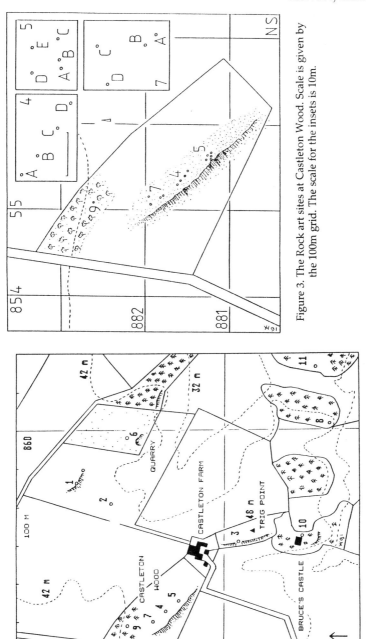

Figure 3. The Rock art sites at Castleton Wood. Scale is given by the 100m grid. The scale for the insets is 10m.

Figure 2. The Rock art sites at Castleton Farm. Scale: 100m squares grid.

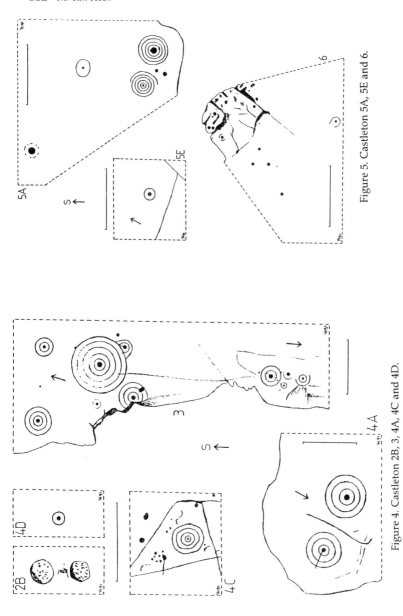

Figure 5. Castleton 5A, 5E and 6.

Figure 4. Castleton 2B, 3, 4A, 4C and 4D.

All scale-bars are 50cm an arrow indicating the magnetic SOUTH is shown outwith all plans. The arrow within each plan indicates the slope of the rock; values mentioned in the text.

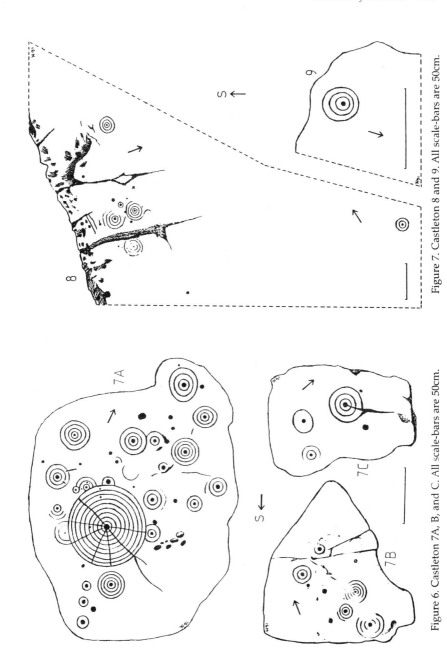

Figure 7. Castleton 8 and 9. All scale-bars are 50cm.

Figure 6. Castleton 7A, B, and C. All scale-bars are 50cm.

BOOK REVIEWS (Historical)

Guide to Scottish Industrial Heritage. Miriam McDonald, editor. Scottish Industrial Heritage Society. 40pp. ISBN 0.9528555.0.X. £2.95.

After a general introduction, good guidance to further reading and information, and maps of grid referenced sites, the expert compiling committee give a site number ordered and referenced gazetteer of more than 200 places of architectural, technical and historic importance in Scotland's industrial past. Over 20 well selected illustrations add to the interest, together with a list of museums with keys to their particular heritage contents, and a subject index to all the sites with over 40 subjects from aqueducts to wool. While the adaptive re-use of former 'heavy' and manufacturing buildings has given way to new 'light' industries quick assembly premises on greenfield sites as more characteristic of industrial heritage today compared with earlier editions, the guide still represents a large increase over the number of sites covered by the last edition in 1985. Some are now museums or main museum features and open to view and study, most others though private may be seen at least externally without special arrangements. Altogether this is a really well produced and authoritative compact guide to a field that attracts much interest in an increasingly leisure orientated society.

From the Forth to the Devon in old picture postcards. Ian Murray. European Library, 'Back in Time' series. 82pp. ISBN 90 288 6303 6. £9.95.

Places featured here are – Cambus, Tullibody, Clackmannan, Kennet, Gartmorn, Sauchie, Fishcross, Coalsnaughton. While some of the 76 pictures are not unfamiliar, all are here well presented and ably annotated There are some of rarer interest e.g. from old late 19th century glass plates are two – The Devon and Linn Mill in winter, and the Devon Colliery beam engine house; also the early 19th century print of ships and the harbour of Alloa seen from the south. As the author notes in his short introduction, this is the third and last of this series of Clackmannanshire photographic histories by him, rounding off a particular story. The first in 1994 was of Alloa itself, the second on the Hillfoots we reviewed in FNH 18 p74 last year. While attractively produced in lasting hardback formats, they are rather costly compared with similar works produced by Stirling Libraries and others.

LC

THE STIRLING PRESBYTERY, 1604-1612:
and the re-imposition of an erastian episcopy

Wayne Pearce
University of Stirling

By looking at the example of the Stirling presbytery, this paper considers the re-imposition in early 17th century Scotland of erastian (state) episcopy in matters related to – presbytery structure and meetings, expectants, moderators, visitations, excommunication; also finance/ministers' stipends, Catholic recusancy, and archaic beliefs and practices.

Stirling presbytery, founded in August 1581, was one of the first 13 presbyteries established "to be exemplars to the rest" (1). The presbytery was intended to be the final link in a hierarchy of church courts comprising the kirk session, presbytery, synod and general assembly; and its creation was the Scottish Reformed Church's response to state and magnate interference in ecclesiastical affairs throughout the 1570s.

From its inception in 1560, the Reformed Church had adopted and advanced the Calvinist doctrines of autonomous ecclesiastical jurisdiction and parity of ministers. Thus the Church met without warrant from the secular authorities and devised policies which subordinated the powers of individual ecclesiastical office holders to the authority of the church courts. Although, in an effort to halt the secularisation of church property, the reformers had been compelled into a series of compromises such as the pseudo-episcopacy at Leith in January 1572 (1a), the Church made it abundantly clear that it regarded the arrangement as an 'interim measure' only. In reality, however, the new bishops, with the encouragement of the State and individual noblemen, were soon asserting their personal authority and defying the ordinances of the General Assembly, the Church's highest juridical authority. By the end of the 1570s the possibility of slipping back to the pre-1560 situation, when episcopal nominations reflected the diplomatic, financial and dynastic interests of the controlling faction of the State, was seen as a very real danger. The restating and redefining of earlier ideals in the *Second Book of Discipline* and the subsequent establishment of the presbytery in 1581 were a reaction to this danger. The presbytery, with its key functions of examination, ordination, admission and deposition of ministers, visitations and ultimate ecclesiastical censure ("the fearful sentence of excommunication") was designed to counter the power and authority of the bishops of old, making them effectively superfluous. Except between May 1584 and June 1586 when presbyteries were proscribed under the terms of the Black Acts, the civil authorities tacitly acknowledged the authority of the presbyteries, though it was not until 1592 that parliament finally and publicly ratified presbyterianism.

No sooner had this been accomplished, however, than attempts began to re-establish an erastian episcopacy in the presbyterian Church of Scotland. The attempts were led by King James VI (1566-1625) who believed it was his divine right to rule over both Church and State, and in the case of the Church, through the episcopate. James was assured that an erastian episcopacy would function as a bulwark to the crown and provide him with control over a Church which while autonomous had not hesitated in chastising the sovereign and his government over their behaviour and handling of matters affecting the spiritual and moral wellbeing of Church and nation. It would also give the king greater control over Parliament and other key institutions through the representation of pliant and sycophantic bishops. Finally, the management by bishops of the nationwide network of church courts would enable the crown to strengthen and extend its influence in the localities.

From the early 1580s James had envisaged an episcopate directly answerable to his person and dependent on him for its standing and authority. He fully approved of the views of archbishop Patrick Adamson who argued in 1581 "that a Christian King sould be the chief governor of the Kirk and behovit to have bischops under him, to hold all in order" (2). Furthermore, the precocious James wholeheartedly backed parliamentary ratification of the Black Acts in May 1584 which established episcopacy and confirmed "the royall power and authoritie over all statis, alsweil spirituall as temporall" (3). However, both internal and external political developments militated against the consolidation and perpetuation of James' episcopate and contributed to its eclipse when the presbyterians regained the initiative in ecclesiastical affairs shortly after the collapse of the regime led by James Stewart, Earl of Arran, in November 1585. The presbyterians largely retained their ascendancy in the Church until December 1596 when the King regained the initiative after the suppression of an anti-Catholic riot in Edinburgh on the 17th of that month. Over the following ten year period James successfully employed various methods to stifle, suppress or by-pass opposition to his programme. By 1606, the General Assembly acknowledged and accepted the royal supremacy and the estate of bishops. By 1610 an erastian episcopacy had been fully restored and received statutory ratification by parliament two years later. While some structural features of presbyterianism remained, the fundamental constitutional and doctrinal characteristics of an autonomous ecclesiastical jurisdiction and parity of ministers were replaced by the royal supremacy and the new hierarchy. Nevertheless like many of their English puritan counterparts the Scottish presbyterians were not prepared to countenance a breakaway from the national church, and were accordingly content to work for its reformation from within.

PRESBYTERY STRUCTURE AND MEETINGS

At its foundation Stirling presbytery comprised 14 churches from the diocese of Dunblane, nine churches from St. Andrews and two detached parishes from the diocese of Dunkeld (Table 1). Between 1581 and the early seventeenth century, a further three churches appear raising the number of parishes within the bounds of the presbytery from 25 to 28. The General

Assembly recognised and addressed the problems facing ministers expected to travel long distances to attend presbyterial meetings when it stipulated in 1598 "that every Presbyterie shall assemble themselves ance orderly ilk week in their full number, at leist so many of them as has thair residence within aught myles to the place of the ordinarie conventione of the Presbyterie" (4).

However, with the exception of George McCallum, the incumbent of Balquhidder from 1608, whose attendance does not occur in the presbytery records, the distance of parishes from Stirling does not appear to have affected attendances at the meetings. On average between 1604 and 1612, ministers registered present or absent varies from 17 to 19 of the possible 30 for the 23 charges (Table 1). There was however a regular turnover and inquisition was taken of consistent absentees, injunctions imposed and fines threatened, which would seemingly confirm that distance from Stirling was not accepted as a justifiable reason for non-attendance.

TABLE 1

PARISH KIRKS	MINISTERS
Airth	Henry Laing
Alloa & Tullibody	James Duncanson
Alva & Tillicoultry	James Gillespie
Bothkennar	James Caldwell
Clackmannan	Richard Wright
Denny	Thomas Ambrose 30/5/03-1/4/07
	James Saitton 3/12/07-6/2/10
	David Forrester 4/4/10
Dollar	Alexander Grieve
Larbert & Dunipace	James Caldwell served these parishes and drew stipend 1607 to 1616
St Ninians	Henry Livingston
Stirling	Patrick Simson
Stirling West/2nd charge	Robert Muir from 29/7/07
Aberfoyle	William Stirling
Balquhidder	George McCallum
Callander, Kilmahog & Leny	Robert Young 9/9 to 1/9/11
	John Mushet from 16/12/12
Dunblane and Kilbride	Andrew Young
	assistant Ninian Drummond
Kilmadock	Malcolm Henrison
Kincardine-In-Menteith	John Aisson
Kippen	William Narne 12/04 onwards
Lecropt	Duncan Nevein to 8/07
	John Dickson 11/08 onwards
Logie	Alexander Hume to 12/9
	James Saittone 2/10 onwards
Port of Menteith	William Stirling
Tulliallan	Henry Forrester
Falkirk (excluded from "Fasti")	Adam Bellenden

While the overall size of the jurisdictional area covered by the presbytery was not a hindrance to its effectiveness, the inclusion of the northern parishes within the diocese of Dunblane did present the presbytery (and the wider Church) with a problem which King James' Highland policy and Lowland attitudes in general compounded. As James Kirk has stated, Dunblane was situated on frontier territory with its northern hinterland in the Gaelic Highlands (5), and while the Reformed Church was continually consolidating and extending its influence in the Highlands, there was clearly a shortage of Gaelic speaking ministers. In August 1611 the Stirling presbytery granted licence to Robert Young to transport himself from the kirk at Callander "becaus the maist part of the saidis prochunnaris speikis onelie the erish language quhilk he undirstandis not. Nather zit do thay undirstand his language" (6). While the statutes of Iona of 1609 provided for the extension of the Church in the Highlands, government/Lowland contempt for and problems with Gaelic language and culture impeded the Church's mission to the populace in the North. It is significant that while John Carswell's Gaelic translation of the *Book of Common Order* in 1567 greatly aided the dissemination of reformed doctrine and practice throughout the Highlands, a Gaelic translation of the New Testament does not appear until 1767, while it is 1801 before the complete Bible is available in Gaelic.

Of the 26 ministers who took an active part in the proceedings of the Stirling presbytery between 1604 and 1612, 19 were known university graduates. In the 12 cases where the name of the university is stated (see Table 2), seven graduated from St. Andrews, three from Glasgow and two from Edinburgh. While there is a need for caution in extrapolating from the above figures, it would appear that a majority of graduate ministers in the Stirling presbytery

TABLE 2

Minister	University	Award and Date of		Ordained
James Duncanson	Glasgow	MA	1585	1589
John Gillespie		MA		1603
James Caldwell		MA		1603
James Saittone		MA		1607
David Forrester		MA		1610
Alexander Grieve		MA		1603
Henry Livingston	St Andrews	MA	1583	1587
Patrick Simson	St Andrews	MA	1574	1577
Robert Muir		MA		1607
John Mushet	St Andrews	MA	1603	1612
Andrew Young	St Andrews	MA	1574	1578
Malcolm Henrison	St Andrews	MA	1581	
John Aison	Edinburgh	MA	1592	1599
William Narne		MA		1604
John Dickson	St Andrews	MA	1595	1608
Alexander Hume	St Andrews	BA	1574	1597
William Stirling	Glasgow	MA	1585	1597
Henry Forrester	Edinburgh	MA	1590	1597
Ninian Drummond	Glasgow	MA	1582	

passed through St. Andrews university where the influence of Andrew Melville, prior to 1606, helped ensure a continuum of ministers imbued with presbyterian doctrine and principles. Although, this in itself is not enough to explain the Stirling presbytery's apparent hostility to the imposition of an erastian episcopacy, it would, nevertheless, appear to be a contributory factor. While it is evident from contemporaneous sources that Patrick Simson, Henry Livingstone, Alexander Hume, Adam Bellenden and Ninian Drummond were hostile to and critical (initially at least) of the re-establishment of episcopacy, there would appear to be no evidence extant which could provide an insight into the attitudes of the other ministers of the presbytery except that which can be deduced from the collective decisions and actions of the presbytery itself.

EXPECTANTS

Also present at presbytery meetings were expectants, who were assigned to make exercises on prescribed passages of scripture. Twelve candidates presented themselves to the presbytery between August 1604 and December 1612, "to give ane tryell of his giftis" (7) (See Table 3). Each having given "ane tryell of his giftis in privie exerceis" (8) of the presbytery on three or four occasions, proceeded to the public exercise and common place if they were found to have "sound and halsum doctrein" (9), where, after further assessment, they were ordained. Expectants provided a necessary function as preachers in vacant parishes. For example, on 27 April 1608, two parishioners of Lekrop appeared before the presbytery with a supplication subscribed to by the lairds of Keir and Knockhill.

"bearand in effect that they ar destitut of ane pastor threw the deceis of umquhille Mr Duncan Nevein and seeing thay electit Mr Johnne Dikson quhome in yair judgement thay think meit to bear yat office desirus ye brethrein to admit him to yame aftur thay have taine tryell of his qualifications." (10)

The presbytery consented to the request and continued to chart and assess Dikson's progress: he was finally ordained and admitted to the charge of Lekrop in November. Having met the canonical requirements of the

TABLE 3

Expectants	Offers Himself	Ordained
William Castellaw	27/03/05	
George Mushet	05/06/05	—
Robert Muir	18/12/05	29/07/07
John Dickson	05/08/07	10/11/08
Robert Young	18/11/07	06/09/09
James Simson	28/09/08	—
Thomas Bruce	31/11/08	—
John Pook	05/04/09	—
David Forrester	17/05/09	03/04/10
John Mushet	/12/11	16/12/12
John Cunningham	04/11/07	—
Patrick Ramsay	/12/11	—

presbytery it was customary for the expectant to have an edict served at the parish to which he was presented informing the parishioners of his appointment and providing them with an opportunity to raise objections. If the placement met with no objection, the presbytery nominated members to carry out the ordination on a prescribed day.

From June 1610, while candidates continued to be examined by the presbytery, they had first of all to present themselves to the bishop, who also had conferred on him the sole rights of ordination. Although there is no episcopal ordination reported in the presbytery records prior to December 1612, there is mention of a letter to the bishop of Dunblane in December 1612 informing him that the presbytery had examined John Mushet, in both private and public exercise as well as in the common place, and found him to have "gude beginnings". In addition, the presbytery went on to advise the bishop that Mushet had as yet not met their full requirements for admission to the ministry. However, the bishop chose to ignore their advice and ordained him four days later.

Unlike the period transcribed by Kirk (11), there are no recorded instances of elders attending Stirling presbytery meetings from 1604 to 1612. However, the absence of elders at Stirling during this period is in accord with the findings of W. R. Foster, who discovered that no elders were listed as either absent or present between 1600 and 1638 in the extensive range of presbytery records which he examined (12). And although the *Second Book of Discipline* stipulated that elders were "to hauld assembleis with the pastouris and doctouris" (13), that document had not originally differentiated the presbytery as a distinct ecclesiastical court. The absence of elders is most likely attributable to the frequency with which the presbytery met. After all, with the presbytery meeting weekly, it would seem impractical to expect elders to attend presbytery meetings in addition to weekly kirk sessions. Whatever the reason, their absence seems to have had no noticeable effect on the court's authority and efficaciousness. Indeed, from the Church's perspective, it was more important that elders, being more often than not local magistrates and landlords, fully supported and helped implement presbyterial ordinances and enactments. Thus, only ministers and expectants enjoyed membership of the Stirling presbytery in the early 17th century. Throughout this period from 1604 to 1612, the presbytery clerk was James Duncanson, minister for Alloa and Tullibody.

MODERATORS

The refusal by the Stirling presbytery to put into effect the decree of the 1606 General Assembly, that each presbytery should accept and implement its nomination of a constant moderator, would appear to show the Stirling presbytery's opposition to the ecclesiastical changes enacted throughout this period. The established method of electing moderators had been to elect a new moderator twice annually. It was common procedure for three nominations "to be given up in lit ... quhairof the moderator to be chosen off quhome be the haill voices" (14). This is in accord with the Calvinist/presbyterian concept of parity of ministers which the acceptance of a constant moderator would have clearly undermined. Six months after the General Assembly's edict, Sir William Livingstone of Kilsyth and John Murray of Touchadame" commissionaris from his Majestais councell" appeared before the presbytery and insisted that the brethren–

"conforme thameselfis to ye conclusiones of ye last meiting in Linlythgow and in speciall according to ane act yairof to receave and authoreis Mr Patrick Simsone as thair constant moderator as lykwise requirit ye said Mr Patrick Simsone to accept the said office" (15).

The presbytery retorted that Simson had been unable to discharge his customary pastoral functions "thrugh seikness thir three monethis bygaine. Meikilles is he habill to dischairge himself as appertainis of the office of ane constant moderator" (16). Subsequently, the commissioners lacked the authority to enforce the election of an alternative constant moderator. Thus, the presbytery's commitment to the doctrine and procedures formulated in the *Second Book of Discipline* "that ane moderator sould be chosine be commoun consent of the haill brethrene conveinit", made it antagonistic towards, and unwilling to implement the General Assembly's injunction. It is worth noting, that while Foster has stated that Jedburgh presbytery was an extreme example in being one of the last presbyteries to yield under threats from the higher ecclesiastical and secular authorities to accept a constant moderator in 1608, Stirling was still nominating moderators bi-annually in 1612. The reason why the General Assembly and government tolerated this dissent is unclear. However, this retention of presbyterian practice turned out to be a pyrrhic victory since its freedom of independent action and thus its authority were emasculated by the loss of its rights of presentation and ordination, also of visitation and, most importantly, excommunication.

VISITATIONS

Visitation of the parishes within the bounds of the presbytery was essentially the sole responsibility of the presbytery until 1610, when the Glasgow Assembly decreed that "the visitatione of ilk diocese is to be done be the bischop himselfe", and although, the act went on to stipulate that the bishop could nominate "worthy men ... in his place", the act was a direct repudiation of established practice. Prior to this date it had been customary for the presbytery to send forth five ministers to conduct visitations. Thus, from 1604 to December 1610, Stirling hospital, Logie, Bothkennar, Lekrop, Alloa, Airth, Falkirk and Dollar parishes were visited and the findings "set doun in ye buik of visitatione". While no books of visitation are known to be extant, visitations followed a similar pattern: the ecclesiastical office holders were examined in turn followed by the general state of the parish and finally difficult disciplinary cases would be scrutinized. From 1610 to 1612 only one proposed visitation is recorded in the presbytery records. On 3 July 1611, a letter from the bishop of St. Andrews was received instructing the presbytery that "he is myndit godwilling to visit the Kirk of Falkirk upone ye fyft day of

July" (17) and requesting ministerial assistance. Although there is no account in the presbytery records of the visitation taking place, there is no reason to suppose it did not. However, the fact that presbyteries could no longer initiate and conduct visitations without the bishop's consent and/or presence curtailed their power. Furthermore, since bishops had a number of civil as well as ecclesiastical functions to perform, visitations were conducted less frequently after 1610.

EXCOMMUNICATION

The most distinctive feature of presbyterial discipline and the principal reason for the presbytery's potency was its right to initiate, supervise and pronounce the sentence of excommunication. Four individuals were excommunicated between August 1604 and December 1612. The process followed a set procedure and accordingly the example of Robert Fairlie will suffice as a standard case. On 15 February 1609, Robert Fairlie of Arnbeg in the parish of Kippen was summoned before the presbytery to answer "for slandering of ye kirk be the cruell slauchter of umquhille Andro Carrik in Arnmoir commited upone ye 111 day of Januar last bypast...." (18). Having been called on more than one occasion prior to this, and again having failed to comply, he was summoned "pro secundo ... under ye paine of excommunicatione" (19). By 22 February he had still not appeared or acknowledged the presbytery's injunction and was summoned "pro tertio to heir and see himself decernyt to be excommunicat for his malitius contempt and disobedience to ye voice of ye kirk...." (20). Finally, on 26 April, William Narne, minister of Kippen, reported that he had admonished Fairlie on four consecutive sabbaths to submit to the discipline of the Kirk, and having failed to comply had excommunicated him on 16 April. Thus, with three summonses followed by four public admonitions plus the sentence itself, the process took a minimum of eight weeks. However, it was common for the process to be stayed if there was any hope of conformity from the impenitent.

Excommunication had serious repercussions for the individual excommunicated, for the ecclesiastical censure could be reinforced by civil penalties. Earlier acts of parliament were strengthened in 1609 when parliament decreed that no excommunicated person "salbe sufferit ... [to] enjoy the possession of thair landis rentis and revenewis, but that the same salbe mellit with, intrometit with and uplift to his majesties use" (21). Therefore, the excommunicated were not simply ostracized from society but also financially ruined. As a result, the overwhelming majority of individuals succumbed to the Kirk's discipline. However, even those who were excommunicated were given the opportunity to repent and have the sentence annulled. On 17 January 1610, the presbytery received a supplication from Robert Fairlie explaining that–

> "he haid pulicit repentence ... in sundrie kirkis many and sundrie dayes according to ye brethreinis ordinence and wald glaidlie proceid in his publict repentence according to ye ordur of ye kirk in all pointis war not he is fairlie informit that his adversar pairtie is haid for him to have his

lyf be the way and yairfor desyris to be absolvit from ye sentence of excommunicatione and receavit in ye kirk...." (22)

The presbytery accepted the sincerity of his repentence and instructed William Narne to absolve him from the said sentence.

The Glasgow Assembly of 1610 seriously curtailed the power and effectiveness of presbyteries when it declared that no sentence of excommunication or absolution be pronounced against or for any individual without first informing the appropriate bishop and gaining his approval. Thus, although the Stirling presbytery could still, technically speaking, initiate and supervise the process of excommunication, it could not pronounce the sentence without firstly obtaining the permission of the bishop of Dunblane or St. Andrews. Furthermore, since the sentence of excommunication could have wide ranging political repercussions, King James (who had insisted in 1605 that no nobleman was to be excommunicated without the consent of the privy council) and his bishops tended to place a higher premium on political expediency rather than canonical authority, and thus excommunication became a rarity after 1610 in all localities.

MINISTERS' STIPENDS

An effective parish ministry throughout the country and within the Stirling presbytery in particular, depended to a large extent upon the provision of a regular and sufficient stipend. To this end, King James' action in 1606 of granting the erection of numerous abbey lands into temporal lordships indirectly benefited the clergy. For in exchange for his statutory recognition of their lands, the lords were asked to provide an adequate stipend to the ministers whose churches had formerly belonged to monastic houses (See Table 4 for churches affected by the enactment). Thus, in 1606 a commission of bishops, ministers and noblemen was established "to set doun and conclude ane sufficient and reasonable stipend for the minister of ilk kirk that salbe conteined in any of the creations" (23). Subsequently, this commission met

TABLE 4 – CHURCHES BELONGING TO FORMER MONASTIC HOUSES

Kirk	Monastric House
Airth	Holyroodhouse Abbey
Alloa & Tullibody	Cambuskenneth Abbey
Alva	Cambuskenneth Abbey
Bothkennar	Cambuskenneth Abbey
Dollar	Inchcolm Abbey
Larbert & Dunipace	Cambuskenneth Abbey
St Ninians	Cambuskenneth Abbey
Leny	Inchmahone Priory
Kilmadok	Inchmahone Priory
Kincardine-In-Menteith	Cambuskenneth Abbey
Kippen	Cambuskenneth Abbey
Lecropt	Cambuskenneth Abbey
Logie	North Berwick Priory
Port of Menteith	Inchmahone Priory

annually and from 1607 until 1611 the Stirling presbytery appointed representatives to appear before the "lordis modifearis of stipendis" (24). However, while many ministers benefited from the above development, others experienced little improvement in their financial status because parliament had omitted to stipulate what an adequate stipend amounted to. Furthermore, no measures were taken to ensure that ministers received the full stipend assigned to them.

Between August 1604 and December 1612 four ministers of the Stirling presbytery are reported as having "na resonabill provisione" (25). Of these four, three were temporal lordships and Thomas Ambrose of Denny, John Gillespie of Alva and Tillicoultry, and Alexander Grieve of Dollar were granted licence to move to alternative charges because their parishioners proved unwilling or unable to provide an adequate stipend. Alexander Grieve complained that his stipend had been appropriated by the titular of the teinds, and although the presbytery elicited a guarantee from the parishioners in August 1608 that each would provide him with "ane boll of victual for his stipend this year allanerlie and sall contribut to mak expensis to sut ane stipend to him in tymes cummin" (26), by 24 January 1610 Grieve reported that the parishioners had reneged on their assurance and gained presbyterial licence to transport himself. The fourth minister, Henry Laing of Airth, first complained in March 1608 that he lacked adequate provision. Nevertheless, a further two years lapsed before he was presented to the parsonage and vicarage of Airth by letters of presentation from both Sir John Bruce of Airth and Alexander, fifth Lord Elphinstone, titular of Holyroodhouse, who each enjoyed the rights of patronage in different areas of the parish. However, this action failed to alleviate Laing's pecuniary problems since he reported on 18 April 1610 that—

"said parsonage is all set in lang takis. Ane pairt yairof to wit the teindis of Elphinstone to My Lord Elphinstone and ye remanent of ye said to ye laird of Airth all for l[a]p li[b] of yeirlie devotie allanerlie quhilk is na sufficient provisione to ane minister to serve the kirk". (27)

Although Laing remained in his charge at Airth there is no indication that he secured additional provision from the above patrons. His failure to gain full possession of the manse and glebe of Airth which was occupied by Cathrine Hamilton, "relict of umquhille Captane James Bruce" (28) despite disbursing £102 Scots on repairs to the said property in April 1608 no doubt compounded his difficulties.

CATHOLIC RECUSANCY

As well as the financial wellbeing of the Church and ministry, the other perennial issue to receive heightened attention during this period was the question of Roman Catholic recusancy. With the excommunication of the Roman Catholic marquis of Huntly and the earls of Errol and Angus in 1608, and the priority given by the Linlithgow assemblies of 1606 and 1608 to combating and eradicating Roman Catholic recusancy, it is worth gauging the extent of Catholic support in the Stirling locality, identifying the forms it took and determining the effectiveness of the presbytery in extirpating it.

The most notorious and persistent recusants in the Stirling locality were the Chisholms of Cromlix. All the bishops of Dunblane between 1487 and 1573 came from this illustrious family, members of which continued to serve the Roman Catholic Church on the continent. Between 1604 and 1612 members of this family and its household servants were called before the Stirling presbytery suspected of papistrie on over 20 different occasions. Other notable recusants called to compear before the presbytery for frequenting neither Word nor Sacrament during this period include James Blackadder, Laird of Tulliallan, Sir Henry Lindsay of Carrestown, and Sir William Menteith of Kerse and his wife Dame Isabel Hamilton. Since it was vitally important that the presbytery received the co-operation and active support of those exercising secular jurisdictions to enhance and enforce its injunctions, the presbytery made strenuous efforts to impose conformity on these local landowners and magistrates.

In the case of James Chisholm, on 23 March 1605 the presbytery "undirstanding that James Chisholme of Cromlikis and Sir Johnne Chisholme fatheris brother ar leatlie returnit" (29), summoned them to compear and give confession of their faith, subscribe to the anti-Roman Catholic *King's Confession* of 1581, receive Holy Communion and submit to the discipline of the Kirk. By the end of May, James Chisholm agreed to frequent "to ye preaching of God His Word" (30) until his imminent departure for the continent. Nevertheless, although James Chisholm, who had been formally excommunicated and subsequently absolved by the Montrose Assembly of 1595, gave an assurance that he would adhere to the Reformed Faith and strictures of the presbytery, he was back in the presbytery's spotlight in August 1608 when Andrew Young, the minister of Dunblane, informed the brethren that he had failed to communicate since 1605. The presbytery demanded that he immediately take Communion in one of the kirks of Kippen, Bothkennar or Tillicoultry, which he complied with by partaking in the Lord's Supper at Tillicoultry on the 14th of August. However, this resulted in controversy when John Gillespie, minister of Tillicoultry, reported on 13 September that "albeit ye said James Chisholme has presented himself to ye Lordis tabill zit he communicat not bot dissembilit yairat" (31). On 28 September he appeared before the presbytery and offered the tenuous excuse that "he nevir communicate off befoir and yairfore he knew not weill the fassone" (32). The revelation that he had not taken Communion in the reformed manner is clearly indicative of the presbytery's difficulty in dealing with prominent and influential individuals within their own localities. The following April, Chisholme took Communion at Stirling with "all reverence and sinciertie" (33) and thus appeased the presbytery. But by August 1610 he was once again reported as absent from the Sacrament, this time with his sisters, Jane and Anna Chisholm.

ARCHAIC BELIEFS AND PRACTICES

In addition to the above conventional form of Roman Catholic recusancy, there were also the superstitions of popular piety. While these were less overtly Catholic, they were nevertheless associated with older beliefs and traditional practices tolerated and even encouraged by the Cambusbarron Chapel or Christ's Well and a belief in the efficaciousness of charms and charmers; on 3 June 1607, 11 individuals were summoned by Stirling presbytery to answer for their idolatrous and superstitious behaviour "and using of diveris superstitius ritis yairat" (34). On 1 July the accused appeared and confessed they "war at Christis Well to gait thair heall of thair disaisis and tak sum of the walter and left sum thing behind everie ane of yame at the well" (35). In response, the presbytery ordered each individual to make public repentence in their respective parish kirks of Airth and Bothkennar. In 1610, a further three persons were admonished and ordered to make public repentance for the same offence. On 11 June 1610, "Mories Scobie in Bahaldie within ye prochun of Dunblane (36) compeared and admitted charming (see appendix for charm used by Scobie) –

'sum seik folkis that sendis for him as Jacobe Zair ane bairne of ye laird of Lundeis callit Collein Campbell ane bairne of Mr James Nevein. Quhilk charme he lernit of Sir Andro Hudsone and preist in Glendoven" (37).

While not conclusive in itself, mention of the laird of Lundy would apparently indicate that these archaic beliefs and practices were not simply confined to a largely uneducated peasantry, but appear to have been adhered to right across the social spectrum. In July 1612, presbytery concluded that "charming is varie frequentlie usit in thir boundis" (38) and instructed each eldership to "tak inquisition quair any sic thing is committed and as they find to tak ordur yairwith as appertanis and to dischairge ye samin publictlie in pulpet" (39). While the retention and perpetuation of these quasi-pagan traditions is a clear indictment of Stirling presbytery's (and wider Scottish Church's) failure to purge their hold over the popular consciousness, it is worth noting that this failure was not peculiar to the Scottish Church, since as Euen Cameron has shown, these traditions were extensively adhered to across Europe and were being observed and complained of in England well into the industrial era (40).

CONCLUSION

To judge from the example of the Stirling presbytery, the effect of the re-imposition of an erastian episcopacy on the power and responsibilities of the presbytery was mixed. In some respects it made little difference. Throughout the period the main functions of the presbytery remained the supervision of the morals and religious convictions of both clergy and laity and most of its work was concerned with cases involving sexual offences and matrimonial disputes. This probably explains why, in contrast to the liturgical innovations of 1617, the imposition of an erastian episcopacy had little impact on the laity of the community and provoked little popular dissent. In other respects however, notably in the changes that were made to the initiation and conduct of visitations and to its powers of excommunication, the adoption of an erastian episcopacy clearly weakened presbytery authority and left the presbytery less effective and authoritative after 1610 than it had been before.

ACKNOWLEDGEMENTS

Quotations from the presbytery record are used with the kind permission of the Keeper of the Records. I wish to express my gratitude to both Dr K. M. Brown and Dr N. L. Tranter at the University of Stirling for their invaluable time and advice.

NOTES AND REFERENCES/SOURCES

1. A Peterkin, The Booke of the Universall Kirk. (1839), p 214, and J. Row, History of the Kirk of Scotland 1558-1639 (1842). p 109.

1a. A chapter of ministers has authority to reject an episcopal vacancy candidate appointed by the Crown, who being at least 30 years of age must swear allegiance to the General Assembly in spiritual matters, and exercise no authority in the Church.

2. J. Melville, Autobiography and Diary of Mr James Melvil. (ed) R. Pitcairn (1842), p 120.

3. A. Peterkin, BUK p 369.

4. Ibid., BUK p 475.

5. J. Kirk, Patterns of Reform, Continuity and Change in the Reformation Kirk. (1989), p 452.

6-10. Stirling presbytery records, CH2/722/4.

11. Stirling presbytery records, SHS, Fourth Series, 17 (1982), introduction by J. Kirk, p 89.

12. W. R. Foster, The Church before the Covenants, The Church of Scotland 1596-1638. (1975), p 89.

13. Second Book of Discipline, BUK, p 546.

14-20. Stirling presbytery records, Ibid., CH2/722/4.

21. Acts of Parliament of Scotland, (ed) T. Thomson, Vol. IV (1816), p 407.

22. Stirling presbytery records, Ibid., CH2/722/4.

23. APS, Vol IV (1816), pp 299-300.

24-39. Stirling presbytery records, CH2/722/4.

40. E. Cameron, The European Reformation. (1991), pp 408-409.

Tables 1-4 have been compiled from the Fasti Ecclesiae Scoticanae. (ed) H. Scott (1920).

APPENDIX

CHARM USED BY MORRIS SCOBIE

The Lord is blessed that heirin is baith mirrie in hairt and hand
The lord is blessed that heirin is he salbe thy warrand
God of his gudeness that he can call and he sendis hestallie
The fusone of middilyird God send it hame to the

The Lord he can, the Lord he zid, he zid syne hestallie
Quha hes bein heir, this nyght he sayes, quha hes bein heir this day
The Elriche King hes bein heir this nyght, and rest fra me away
The pouar of woman and mankynd, and bayth sone grant thow me

The fusone of mirrie middilyird he hes tane fra me away
Grant me the gift sone againe that I granted to the
Or ellis thow sall have hell to thy dwelling and damisday at zo'dur
The father the sone and holy gaist and him
I laive with thee.

Sir Andro Hudson, priest in Glendevon
(CH2/722/4)

BOOK REVIEWS (Historical)

Buchlyvie: a village in Stirlingshire. J. R. Bureau. Stirling Library Services. 64pp. ISBN 1.870.542.33.9. £3.95.

Temptingly presented in a two colour generous format, well illustrated with photos, drawings, and maps of 1817, 1850, 1890s and 1914. Stirling Libraries have given us another commendable contribution to the history of the area, including an innovative four page list of local people and their role through the ages e.g. John Campbell, 'Red Black' Colporteur c.1920. Useful further references are given and acknowledgements to local people who have contributed much additional to the usual sources. From pre-history, through the beginnings 1500-1800, the 19C and the last 100 years, people, places, events are succinctly told and illustrated, including the confrontations with Rob Roy and the MacGregor cattle reivers. George Dixon briefly contributes the 'founding' of the village by a Charles II charter of 1672, having the 'shape' of a Carolingian planned settlement – typical of pre-Georgian types.

Menstrie, a People's History. John Anderson, Clackmannan Libraries. 64pp. £4.

Generously spaced A4 format with some illustrations, this is a fact-full, readable presentation of the origins, people, industry, social conditions, church and events, characters, customs – admirable and desirable local history.

Further Notes On The District Of Menteith

2. JOHN GRAHAM OF DUCHRAY 1600-1700
People of the Forth (10)

Louis Stott

It would have been very interesting if, in his *Notes on the District of Menteith*, R.B. Cunninghame Graham had explored one character from the past who might have measured up to him. This was John Graham, the seventeenth century laird of Duchray, known as 'The Tetrarch of Aberfoyle'. Cunninghame Graham mentions his fellow clansman, but allows his attention to focus upon the Earl of Glencairn, rather than on Graham, the Earl's principal lieutenant.

Notes on the District of Menteith provides, in a series of elegant, witty and quite inimitable essays, an idiosyncratic picture of the history and topography of the area. "From the earliest ages Menteith was one of the five great districts into which Scotland was divided. Its ancient history, down to the creation of the earldom in the twelfth century, was as shadowy and indefinite as that of most parts of Scotland at the time," he begins, and goes on to relate how the Comyn and Stewart Earls of Menteith ruled a great province, but the last of them, Murdoch Stewart, Duke of Albany, over-reached himself in the capacity of Regent and, in 1425, the medieval Earldom of Menteith was broken up by James I. Some of the lands of the former Earldom (Aberfoyle, and a part of the Port of Menteith) were reconstituted as the Earldom of Menteith, and granted to Malise Graham (formerly Earl of Strathearn) in 1427. At this time the lands of Duchray were a Royal deer forest, a part of the Stewartry of Menteith, as the lands outside the re-constituted Earldom were known. There were extensive oak and birch woodlands populated by game, with, later, some ironworkings (bloomeries), as can be seen to this day, for example, at Sronmacnair. Malise was descended from Robert II, so the Graham Earls of Menteith, and their cadets (including Cunninghame Graham himself), could claim descent from a King of Scots.

There were numerous minor Grahams, easily confused with one another, who were granted or held land in Menteith. By the reign of Charles I, William Graham, the seventh earl, had become one of the most powerful men in Scotland. However, rather like Albany before him, he may have begun to have delusions of grandeur. He sought to establish his title to the Earldom of Strathearn, and, according to his detractors, may have asserted that his blood was 'the reddest' in the Kingdom. This called into question the King's title to his Crown, a singularly unwise course of action. Menteith was soon cut down to size, and offered what Cunninghame Graham called a 'pantomimic' title, that of Earl of Airth. His successor, grandson William, was the last proper Graham Earl of Menteith. The Grahams of Duchray survived much longer than this, at least partly because they occupied lands outside the reconstituted

Earldom. In 1528 we know that a part of the Forest of Duchray was occupied by a George Buchanan who was engaged in ironworking. This land was sold to John Graham (of Dounans) in 1569. His son, William Graham, probably erected Duchray Castle at the end of the C16. A.S.MacNair in *Queen Elizabeth Forest Park* (1973) notes a charter requiring the building of a castle by 1514. William Graham seems to have died in 1618. His son John, who became John Graham of Poldar, and then the 'bonnet-laird' of Gallingad, was an ancestor of R.B. Cunninghame Graham. He sold Duchray to a different Graham, Thomas Graham of Inchrie in 1622. Inchrie was adjacent to Duchray, and a house of that name is part of the present Covenanters' Hotel.

Our subject John Graham of Duchray, son of the above Thomas, married Marion Graham of Rednock, a direct descendant of the 4th Graham Earl of Menteith, and so inherited Rednock. Known as 'Highland Hector', and 'the Tetrarch of Aberfoyle', he became the brother-in-law of Alexander Colquhoun of Camstradden when the latter married Marion Graham's younger sister, Anne, in 1644. Curiously, we learn more of him from Wm. Fraser's *Chiefs of Colquhoun* (1869) than from the same author's *Red Book of Menteith* (1880). Without comment Fraser states that Duchray was born in 1600, and died in 1700. The district, as Rev. Patrick Graham pointed out in *Sketches of Perthshire* (1806), is noted for longevity, although John Graham of Duchray was not one of the two instances which the scholarly minister quoted. Whether Duchray lived to be a hundred or not, he certainly deserves attention. He is known to have loaned money to Charles II, and Fraser states that he fought alongside Montrose who presented him with a silver pistol. 'The souvenir, which is still preserved in the repositories of the Duchray family, John Graham would at no time part with, wearing it by day, and putting it under his pillow at night' (Fraser).

In 1653-54 John Graham of Duchray played a key part in the Earl of Glencairn's Rising The ninth Earl, William Cunningham, resided at Finlaystone, an estate across the Clyde from Dumbarton, and came to Duchray in August 1653, with Charles II's commission to raise a rebellion in his pocket, and at Aberfoyle he raised his first troops. One of the few successes which his Rising enjoyed was here at Aberfoyle. Duchray accompanied him to the Highlands, and is said to have written the account on which much of our knowledge of the Earl's campaign is based. Published in 1822 (see appendix) this was edited by Sir Walter Scott whose attention may well have been drawn to it by Reverend Patrick Graham, the learned Minister of Aberfoyle, who did much to inform Scott about Perthshire legends. The author is described as "a person who was eye and ear witness to every transaction", but, in a footnote, Scott attributes the work to Graham of Duchray. He goes on to acknowledge, in another footnote, that he shifted the events of this campaign of Cromwell's time, in the one case forwards, to give us Colonel Thornton's expedition in *Rob Roy* and, in the other backwards, to immortalise Helen Stewart in The Lady of the Lake. Another of the dramatis personae, Colonel Wogan, appears in *Waverley*. Duchray's account of the Rising was, of course, partial. Other accounts differ, but what John Graham had to say about what he knew, rings true. For example, it is his account of the celebrated duel between Glencairn and his successor's second-in-command that has gone down in history. The noted C19 historian John Hill Burton characterised this event as "having the picturesqueness that might suit a novel-writer", but Duchray's narrative does not seem to have been used in this way until Nigel Tranter's recent novel *Honours Even* (1995). In his *Notes* Cunninghame Graham muses wittily on the duel, and the summary execution that followed it.

Duchray himself was involved in the first successful skirmish at the Pass of Aberfoyle in early September 1653. It is not clear whether, when Glencairn came South again in March 1654, Duchray came with him, or whether he was involved with MacNaughten in a skirmish in Menteith in April which resulted in victory for Cromwell's troops. This episode probably provoked the letter from Monck, who had just arrived in Scotland, to the Earl of Airth desiring him to "give order for the cutting down" of woods about Milton and Glassert which harboured "loose, idle and desperate persons". The Earl seems to have failed to do this, because towards the end of the Rising, Monck himself, who reported the fact to Cromwell, was encamped in the neighbourhood of Aberfoyle in August 1654. "We are now destroying this place", he boasted, "which was the chief recepticle to the enemy last winter". However, there were reports in *Mercurius Politicus* on 14th December 1654 that there were 'a few' moss troopers with Duchray on the braes of Menteith. It was not until after this that matters were resolved.

John Graham of Duchray was the very last of the rebel lairds to lay down his arms, on 17th July 1655, almost a year after the Rising, as such, was supposed to have been brought to an end. He was described by a contemporary historian (Baillie) as "amongst the most honest, stout and wise of them all". Monck drew up a treaty with Duchray, as he had with such distinguished lairds as Tullibardine and Seaforth (Seaforth having, it is said, suggested that he would make peace if he could have the hand of Cromwell's daughter in marriage!). By the treaty Duchray gave up his arms, but was permitted to keep a small band of armed men to defend his land, provided that he ensured that rebels and thieves were not harboured there. The forty or so soldiers raised by Duchray were, it is said, never stood down, and became part of the Black Watch (the 'forty-twa') (Louisa Graeme *Or and Sable*). It is generally asserted that the Black Watch got their name from their dark tartan, and became the 42nd Regiment as a result of their supposed order of seniority in the line. Such companies were called 'Watches', and their principal function in times of peace was to guard against the depredations of cattle and sheep thieves, nowhere more prevalent than in West Perthshire. They were sustained by a rent - 'black mail or watch money' - and it would be surprising if they were not referred to as the 'Black Watch'. The names carry these significant echoes of Aberfoyle. During the C18 and C19 the Grahams of Duchray were prominent soldiers in the Black Watch.

During the campaign Duchray looked after the late Marquis of Montrose's son and heir, James Graham (1631-1669), then a young man, later known as 'the Good Marquis'. The Grahams of Menteith were distant relations of the Grahams, Earls, Marquises and, later, Dukes of Montrose. It is also interesting to note that, on the death of the 15th Earl of Glencairn in 1796, the Grahams of Gartmore succeeded, and thus became Cunninghame Grahams. After the Restoration in 1661, Duchray played a prominent part in the true Funeral of Montrose. He carried the great Pincel (streamer) bearing the Duke's arms. In February 1671 Graham of Duchray was involved in a notorious fracas at the Bridge of Aberfoyle with the last Earl of Menteith and of Airth, when he, Duchray, and his son Thomas, were going to the baptism of a grandchild by the then Minister of Aberfoyle, Reverend McVicar. The Earl perceived the ceremony as an opportunity to recover money from Duchray and in the ensuing skirmish (the baby was set down on the ground) the Earl's party was driven off. Duchray was duly cautioned at the Tolbooth in Edinburgh to keep the peace. In 1686 James VII recompensed Duchray "for his loyalty, services and sufferings". At this time the Buchanans of Drymen, and the Earls of Menteith had become impoverished, and James Graham, the third Marquis of Montrose acquired their lands in 1680. It was then that he moved to Buchanan House.

It was Graham of Duchray (whether John, or his son Thomas, is not clear), who was also present at an even more famous baptism, that of the Reverend Robert Kirk's posthumous daughter. It is said that when Kirk's wraith appeared at the christening Duchray, "by some unaccountable fatality" failed to cast a dagger above Kirk's head to release him from 'fairyland'. This famous story was set down by a successor Rev. Patrick Graham in *Sketches of Perthshire*, who stated that "Mr Kirk was the near relation of Graham of Duchray, the ancestor of the present General Graham Stirling". He goes on to say that Kirk's wraith first appeared to "a mutual relation of his own, and of Duchray". Who this might have been we do not know, nor is the precise relationship, if any, between Kirk and Graham of Duchray clear. However, it can be observed that, if Fraser is to be believed, Duchray would have been 92 years of age when this incident is supposed to have taken place which makes his failure to cast the dagger understandable.

Whether this is an accurate account of John Graham of Duchray's life or not, we know enough to assert that he must have been a remarkable man. Fraser reports that he was laconic, writing to his wife from London in the days of Charles 1: "My dearest Marion, the King's well, the Queen's well, and if you're well, all's well, your affectionate husband, John Graham". Fraser also states that, unlike some of his equals, he was literate, and could draw up documents himself, perhaps having been educated as a notary. We know that he was honest, wise, loyal and brave. He should occupy a very respected place in the annals of Aberfoyle.

In 1724 his grandson Alexander Graham (probably the baby set on the ground in 1671) wrote, in 1724, a number of very significant descriptions of the district which were included in MacFarlane's *Geographical Collections*. Alexander Graham was a contemporary of Rob Roy, and it may have been his sisters who are said by some to have smuggled Rob Roy out of Duchray Castle while they entertained a party of Dragoons, though genealogists do not record that Alexander had any sisters. It is often stated that Duchray Castle was burned both in 1653 and in 1715, and sometimes said that the castle was not occupied for a hundred years thereafter. However, in 1724, in his description of the Parish of Drymen, Alexander Graham refers to the castle (his), as an attractive residence.

He married Margaret Stirling of Achyll in 1718, uniting the Grahams with a branch of another notable family, the Stirlings of Keir. The Duchrays inherited that estate as well as Rednock in 1797, and became the Graham Stirlings of Duchray, Rednock and Achyll. The last Graham Stirling died in 1875. The estate then passed to Rev. Henry Alan Graham Sheppard whose great nephew sold Duchray in 1949. Duchray thus passed out of the hands of the Grahams.

Appendix
The Earl of Glencairn's Rising

The Earl of Glencairn's expedition is said to have been a very bad imitation of Montrose's expedition ten years earlier. Glencairn was appointed to his command by Charles II, but only because the experienced Middleton (who was second in command to Leslie at Philiphaugh, and was with the Scots at Worcester) was not available. In August 1653 Glencairn held a meeting of chiefs at Lochearnhead, and six weeks later his expeditionary force began to assemble rather desultorily in the neighbourhood of Aberfoyle. Their first engagement took place in the Pass of Aberfoyle, and they were successful in driving off the greater part of a regiment of foot under the command of Colonel Read from Stirling Castle.

This relatively minor success brought more recruits. When Glencairn marched northwards to Lochearnhead, and then to Loch Rannoch he was joined by Atholl, Glengarry and Locheil. One of the chiefs who had turned up at the first meeting was the legendary Farquharson of Inverey who was assembling men in Braemar on Deeside, and Glencairn made to join him. However, the English Colonel Morgan, then in Aberdeen, cut Glencairn off, and he was forced to retire to Badenoch by a pass leading to the forest of Abernethy

> "which he was enabled to reach chiefly by the bravery of Graham of Duchray, who, at the head of a resolute party of 40 men, kept in check a body of the enemy who had entered the glen before the royalists, and prevented them from securing the passes." (Graham)

Glencairn and his army then lay in Badenoch awaiting further reinforcements. In due course Lord Lorn arrived with a considerable body of Campbells, but, owing to some dispute, took them away again on 1st January, 1654. Glencairn sent Glengarry and Locheil after them, and they caught up with the defectors near Ruthven castle. Glengarry might have attacked them but, using Graham of Duchray as a negotiator, Glencairn persuaded the Campbell foot soldiers to rejoin him, but they soon deserted again.

Glencairn next invested Kildrummie castle without taking it, and then occupied Elgin. At this point (March 1654) Middleton, with the King's Commission now making him Commander-in-Chief, appeared in Sutherland. Glencairn therefore crossed the Ness and met him at Dornoch where a review of the assembled troops took place. In Middleton's eyes the number of troops he had been promised had been greatly exaggerated, and he regarded the army as a disappointment. Glencairn and the chiefs, who had survived the winter and crossed the Highlands by storm bound passes, regarded their men with pride. Neither man was really suited to the command: Glencairn was a lowlander, not really acceptable to the Highland chiefs, somewhat emotional and probably too gentlemanly, but at least he was an Earl; Middleton, who had a lower status, was even less acceptable to them, and he was an unscrupulous and blustering sort of commander. When Glencairn rode along the ranks - 3500 foot soldiers and 1500 mounted men - to tell them that he was no longer their General, and that he hoped they would serve Middleton loyally, some men "both officers and soldiers shed tears, and vowed that they would serve with their old general in any corner of the world" (Graham). After this Glencairn gave a banquet in Dornoch to Middleton at which he proposed a toast to his gallant army. Thereupon Middleton's second in command, Sir George Munro, rose from his seat and said that the men he had seen were nothing, but a gang of "thieves and robbers". This outraged Glengarry who was, however, restrained by Glencairn who insisted that the quarrel was between him and Munro. Then and there Middleton did his best to patch up the quarrel, but he was unsuccessful.

A celebrated duel between the two followed this incident. After the banquet Glencairn and Duchray and others returned to their quarters, four miles south of Dornoch. The challenge was issued when Glencairn, Duchray and Colonel Blackadder were drinking with the laird with whom they were lodged, and whose daughter was playing the virginals. Munro's brother appeared, and Glencairn made a great fuss of him. Duchray relates that, while the rest of the party were dancing, Munro's brother and Glencairn stepped outside for a few moments, exchanged a few words, and the visitor left after another drink. Glencairn did not confide in Duchray, but, after just two hours sleep, he got up and fought Sir George Munro early the next morning on the links at Dornoch. Munro was seriously hurt, but Glencairn is given credit for having desisted from killing him, although it was his manservant who was said to have held his hand. Glencairn was thereupon arrested by Middleton, but was later released. A second duel on the links followed a week later between two officers, one of whom supported Munro, the other Glencairn. Glencairn's man killed Munro's; Middleton had him arrested and shot, inspite of an intercession by Glencairn. Unsurprisingly, the rift between the two generals widened, and Glencairn left what has always been known as 'his' Rising, going to Assynt (see Note1), then Kintail and finally Killin. Typically, he regretted his own conduct, and sent the forces he had gathered to join Middleton.

Monck returned to Scotland in April 1654, and in July Middleton was routed by Morgan at Dalnaspidal. This is considered to have brought the Rising to an end, although independent chiefs continued to make trouble in various parts of the Highlands. Indeed, in a letter to Cromwell describing Morgan's victory, Monck mentions that Glencairn was at Loch Lomond with about 200 horse, and that "Forrester, MacNaughton and others [were] joined with him about Aberfoyle" this made up 500 horse and foot. Glencairn successfully attacked Dumbarton Castle, but he capitulated in September 1654 at the foot of Dumbarton Rock, and the Marquis of Montrose capitulated shortly afterwards. There were press reports of rebels with Duchray on the Braes of Menteith in December of that year, and John Graham of Duchray did not capitulate until July, 1655.

Note 1. A further interesting, if confusing, connection between the Rising in the Highlands and Aberfoyle is provided by a prediction made by a seer near Ullapool in May 1653 which was quoted by Sir George Mackenzie of Tarbat (1630-1714) in a well-known letter to Robert Boyle as an instance of second sight. Robert Kirk first published the letter in *The Secret Commonwealth*. The prediction stated that English troops leading horses would turn them loose to eat barley in a nearby field. The prediction was made in the presence of Lord Tarbat four or five days before barley was sown in the field. Tarbat questioned the seer, asking him how he knew that they were English troops and received a reply describing the way they dressed. "In the beginning of August thereafter, the Earl of Middleton, having occasion to march a party of his towards the South Highlands, sent his foot through a place called Inverlaewell [Inverlael], and the forepart which was the first down the hill, did fall to eating the barley...". Lord Tarbat's report cannot be right because it was in the summer of 1654 that Middleton was active in the Highlands. It can also be observed that Middleton's army were mainly highlanders; it was General Monk who was at the head of the 'English' army, but he did not take them so far North. However, Glencairn did go to Assynt earlier in the year, and Middleton sent a party in pursuit of him in the Spring of 1654. Middleton and Munro, with the remnants of their troops, were probably in Sunderland in August, 1654 after their defeat at Dalnaspidal.

References and Further Reading:

Baillie, (Rev) Robert *Letters and Journals* (1841)
Chambers, Robert *Domestic Annals of Scotland* (1859-61)
Cunninghame Graham, R.B. *Notes on the District of Menteith.* (1895)
Fraser Wm. *Chiefs of Colquhoun* (1869)
Fraser, Wm. *Red Book of Menteith* (1880)
Keltie, John S. *History of the Highlands*
Napier, Mark *Life of Montrose* (1856)
Scott, Sir Walter (Ed.) *Military Memoirs of the Great Civil War* (1822)
Scottish Record Office *Records of the Army Council of Scotland*

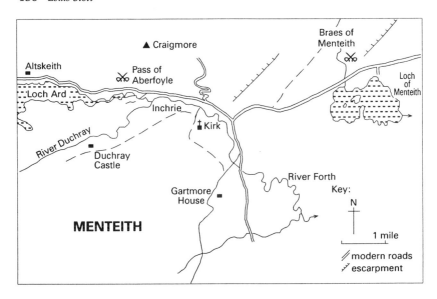

Duchray Castle and its environs.

BOOK REVIEWS (Historical)

For The Lion: A History of the Scottish Wars of Independence, 1296-1357.
Raymond Paterson. John Donald. 208pp. £9.95. ISBN 0 85976 435 4

It is astonishing, given the obvious public and academic interest in the Anglo-Scottish wars of the fourteenth century (even before Braveheart!), that this is the first book to cover the period as a whole. Mr Paterson asserts quite rightly that the Treaty of Northampton-Edinburgh of 1328 - which recognised Scotland's independence - acted merely as a slight stumbling-block to the ambitions of the English crown; he is to be commended for seeking to remedy this rather obvious flaw in Scottish historiography.

The author also has an obvious knowledge of, and interest in, military history; the book is thus noteworthy for the integration of discussions on the development of military techniques with the narrative, even if the former sometimes threatens to overshadow the latter. The book is also easy to read, although it is debatable whether Mr Paterson succeeds in bringing history alive, as he hopes (the length of the period covered perhaps precludes this), despite some flowery touches.

And what about the history itself? The author is clearly a 'Bruce man' and this predetermines the narrative as essentially the story of the inexorable drive of the Scottish nation towards its rightful free and independent state, not least through the efforts of the great hero-king. Nothing wrong with that, the reader might say, and Mr Paterson will agree with you. The big question (and one that can be asked of so many of the books written on this period) is, does that help us to understand the conditions of the fourteenth century and the beliefs and motivations of contemporaries, or does it tell us more about the political desires and prejudices of our own time? Mr Paterson certainly attempts to give us all the facts; however, by having predetermined the overall thrust of the narrative, he is often either unable to answer the questions which these facts inevitably raise, or else provides some most unconvincing arguments to explain them.

This is perhaps most evident in the treatment of the Balliols, father and son. The traditional view of King John as a man of irredeemable spinelessness (meaning here, presumably, the tendency to bend over backwards to accommodate the wishes of Edward I) is accepted without question, completely ignoring the fact that he was subject to one of the most thorough historical propaganda campaigns, perpetrated by the man who ousted him, Robert Bruce. It is certainly true that Balliol was blessed with indifferent military skills and, indeed, too great a degree of timidity, a serious flaw in a medieval monarch but by no means fatal if he is willing to delegate, as Balliol was. In administrative terms, the evidence for King John's brief reign, which includes the reorganisation of the north-west into sheriffdoms, indicates that, if left to his own devices, he would have continued to extend the power of the Crown in exactly the same manner as Alexander III.

Indeed, if one wants an example of extreme 'spinelessness', one need look no further than Robert Bruce the Competitor (grandfather of the king). This man would have gone to any lengths in pursuit of the throne: initially he suggested to Edward I that the latter should advance his claim of overlordship before choosing a king (though doubtless Edward had already thought of that); finally, Bruce changed the thrust of his legal argument when he seemed likely to lose, joining with John Hastings in denying that Scotland was a kingdom at all and asserting that it should be divided equally among the three descendants of David, Earl of Huntingdon. To suggest that it was Balliol who lacked honour (p.22) does little credit to the facts, nor to the members of the Scottish political community who fought thereafter in defence of their king.

How does one explain that support? Were the Scots uniformally stupid in adhering to a man who, supposedly, had proved how little he valued them and Scotland itself? Or was King John more politically aware than Mr Paterson, who does not consider that the condemnation of the Scots issued by Balliol in 1299 might well have been an attempt to fool King Edward into believing that he could safely be released from English captivity, as happened shortly thereafter [p.21-2]. Balliol would never have been a great king, but he does not deserve the historical reputation created for him by his usurper; after all, we would hardly look to Henry VII to write a glowing testimonial to Richard III.

Edward Balliol fares little better in the latter part of the book, despite the author's own analysis of many of the events in which he took part. There can be little doubt that the unease which many Scots felt towards the exclusion of the Balliols from the throne lessened with the death of King John in 1313 and the passage of time generally; equally, the fact that the hand of England was clearly discernible behind Edward Balliol would have put off even those who were sensible to the legitimacy of his claim. Nevertheless, Edward's own actions should be given some credit: his military affairs were attended with some success, all of which should not be laid at the door of others; if he made mistakes, it should be remembered that Robert Bruce was also guilty of grave errors in his first year. Balliol's greatest weakness, as Mr Paterson admits, lay with the fact that he was not a free agent but subject to the excessive demands made upon him by Edward III and the Disinherited.

But even when things went well for Balliol, he is given no credit. The highpoint of his administration in 1333 is dismissed in the following terms:
"And yet even at its most secure Balliol's rule has an impermanent character: attendance of the native nobility at his two parliaments was extremely weak; no accounts have come down to us from William Bullock, his chancellor; and he never issues his own coinage. Throughout this whole period there was a small body of patriots who would not be reconciled to his rule; but there also seems to have been an even larger group who remained on the sidelines, supporting neither one party nor the other, simply waiting to see how things turned out."

But could not such an analysis have applied equally well to King Robert's regime until 1309 at least, if not later? The difference is, of course, that we know that Bruce wins out, and Balliol does not. Naturally contemporaries did not have this benefit and thus had to make decisions according to the circumstances as they found them.

Double standards are equally applied to the Bruce campaign in Ireland. This venture, though ultimately a rather dismal failure, makes some sense, from King Robert's viewpoint, as an attempt to bring Edward II to the negotiating table. However, it is very easy to ignore the fact that the Scots, whose actions indicate that they were bent on conquest, were welcomed by only a tiny minority of the native Irish (for their own political ends) and became absolutely detested as their campaigns wore on in years of extreme famine. It is extraordinary how quick we are to condemn the actions of Edward I, only to avert our eyes from the consequences of a policy which, to the Irish, must have looked remarkably similar.

In the final analysis, this book provides a good basic account of the events of this important period, give or take a few factual errors[1]. This is in itself of value, since no other book provides such an account and students and those interested in the subject generally will thus find it of considerable use as a starting point. However, in terms of illuminating the complexities of the period, providing an understanding of the difficult choices, the conflicting loyalties and the varying interpretations of what was right facing the members of this *medieval* society, the reader is left as ignorant as before reading. This book, as with so many others, makes it all seem so very simple; the reason why it is so simple becomes clear in the final two pages of the book, which degenerates into pure political polemic. Mr Paterson is at least honest in declaring his agenda, where others are more disingenuous.

However, in seeking to judge those that lived seven hundred years ago by a modern set of beliefs which are by no means universally accepted today, he unwittingly does Scotland's history a grave disservice. For so long as we continue to expect no more of our past than a metaphorical pat on to the back, a comforting warm feeling that once we done good, our history will be of interest only to ourselves. Once we accept that Robert Bruce in particular represents only one point of view, and not necessarily, on all occasions, the most prevalent one, once we acknowledge that voices which dissented from the official version of events pedalled by the winners must be listened to in order to understand the period as a whole, then we will be in a position to make the rest of the world sit up and take notice. There is every reason to be proud of Scotland's past, but it is only by acknowledging its complexity that the usual mythology of heroes and villains will be turned into the history of a very human struggle where political rights and wrongs seem clear-cut only to future generations and the outcome is never predestined. That is the real lesson of Scotland's past; it might also have relevance for the future.

Fiona Watson

---

[1] Many of these slips could easily have been avoided by the use of G.W.S. Barrow's third edition of *Robert Bruce and the Community of the Realm of Scotland* (1988). It is slightly astonishing that this book was not consulted.

Wallace, Bruce, and the War of Independence by Antony Kamm. Illustrated by Jennifer Campbell. Scottish Children's Press. 1996 64 pp. £4.95.

The need for well-written, balanced and entertaining accounts of Scotland's history for children is more pressing even than the shortage of such books for adults. Up to a point, this book certainly helps to fulfill such a need. It is a slim volume, which makes it all the more accessible to a younger audience; equally, the illustrations are both dramatic and evocative, illuminating the text in every sense.

The blurb on the back cover makes a number of fairly weighty claims, not least that the book does "full justice" to "a tremendous story", while at the same time presenting "a fair and balanced picture". These claims are not wholly unjustified and it is clear that the author has done a considerable amount of reading. The battles - most particularly Stirling Bridge and Bannockburn - are very well done, making the most of the available evidence while at the same time creating an undeniable sense of atmosphere. On the other hand, in other detailed descriptions (and there is a considerable amount of detail) there are far too many errors for comfort. More importantly, despite the claims of a "fair and balanced picture", the author does not always differentiate between what is legend and what is documented history. The young reader is still, therefore, encouraged to accept as known facts many of the popular myths written down almost two centuries after the events by Blind Hary.

It is vitally important that young Scots learn the history of their country (in addition to other histories). However, there is no reason why they cannot also be introduced to the idea that history is complex. This book is certainly not patronising and perhaps, in fact, goes too far in trying to present as many facts as possible within the space. Nevertheless, the interpretation of these facts is, on many occasions, decidedly simplistic (with some fine exceptions). If the book had no pretensions in this respect, then there should be no criticism. Given the depth of information presented, which might prove rather intimidating to younger children, the author might well have come closer to fulfilling the claims made for the book. However, he is not alone in finding that reconciling the stirring myths with the less enthralling history is a highly problematic business; he is to be commended for making as good a job of it as he has.

Fiona Watson

Editor's Note: relating to Scotland's history for children.

Fiona Watson's review of the Kamm/Campbell book above emphasises the need for effective children's books like this, so it seems relevant to recall that Central Region Education produced in 1984 a 100 page A4 teachers resource book *Scotland During the Wars of Independence*. Well researched and referenced, innovatively written and illustrated this is one of their three teachers aids seeking to relate Scottish history events to what was going on in places in this area of mid-Scotland. The other two were *The Jacobites* and *Changing Society 1750-1800*.

Thornhill and its Environs : A Social History. Stuart J. McCulloch. Munro Trust and Stirling Library Services. 1996. 149pp. ISBN 1-900489-40-6. £7.50.

Following the appearance in FNH last year of 'The Founding of Thornhill in 1696' (vol. 18, pp. 75-82), the Menteith village has been en fête at intervals during its tercentenary year, its varied celebratory programme a model of how a small community should mark a round-number anniversary. Published at the time of the programme's principal week, in June 1996, this book by a current resident of Thornhill is the first about the settlement's past and offers a readable and at times entertaining, if lightweight, account of two millennia or so of human life in the Thornhill vicinity. Of the 41 short chapters, six deal with the years from prehistory to Rob Roy, 13 with the founding and growth of the village, 12 with the 'The Victorian Era' and nine with the first half of this century, with two pages by way of postscript on the village since 1945. Heavily based on secondary sources, the book suffers for much of its length however – even allowing for the narrowing sense of the subtitle – from the traditional weakness so common in parish histories: the "write all you know about ..." approach, where a trawl through local statistical accounts, guidebooks, only partly indexed newspapers and the like produces an aggregation of colourful incidents and anecdotes without resulting in a representative consideration of key aspects of the area's past.

On the errors of commission side, space permits the correction of only a few of the more egregious. The 1745-46 Jacobite rebellion was not "smaller" than those in 1708 and 1715 (p. 32); Lord Kames, having died in 1782, did not begin the clearance by water of Kincardine Moss in 1783 (p. 36); a "cruciform shape" was not "the most popular of the designs for the Georgian planned village" (p. 39, where the nameless plan displayed is largely irrelevant to Thornhill); Thornhill and Norrieston cannot have "joined together" by the late 18th century (p. 39) though still "separate" in "in 1866" (*recte* 1862-3, p. 52); the column of figures on p. 40 lists not the values of local estates in 1771 but their "valued rents" (i.e., their real rents as long before as 1656); its was not the 18th century that saw "the great public advances" of "electoral reform and the health, housing and factory acts" but the 19th (p. 64); no anachronistically early pipe band performed in Thornhill in 1858 (p. 66); 1845 was not "in the middle of the 18th century" (p. 73), and the Napier whose "ideas were very much English", according to Ramsay of Ochtertyre, was not the founder of Thornhill but his distant and later relative, Francis, Lord Napier (p. 74).

Since Thornhill's historical significance lies chiefly in its being a pre-Georgian planned village of known origin, the heart of the volume for the general reader lies in its account of the years 1695-96 (pp. 25-28). Apart from the author's mistranscriptions and occasional unfounded speculations, this section is almost entirely based on this reviewer's primary-source research as presented in FNH 18; whether the fact is adequately acknowledged in the work under review is for the readers of both publications to judge. The volume is extensively illustrated and colourfully covered.

G. A. Dixon

MAN AND THE LANDSCAPE SYMPOSIA

The 22nd annual symposium in this series on 16 November 1996 is on the theme Environmental Awareness and Education, with ten short presentations by key people/organisations in the environment/sustainability field – the last being a demonstration of HSE (Heart of Scotland Environment) a multimedia CD-ROM resource for schools based freely on FN&H's book/survey *Central Scotland – land, wildlife, people.*

These symposia started in the year after the British Association for the Advancement of Science (BA)'s meeting at the University in 1974, as a number of people, particularly in the University, were anxious that such presentations of general interest should be regular and not just once a lifetime – since BA meetings are annually at universities and hence have a 40-year plus cycle!

The first Man and the Landscape of 1975 was organised by Lindsay Corbett, the Clackmannanshire Field Studies Society, and Robert Innes, University Continuing Education. Following the BA meeting also, several University staff and others in 1975 inaugurated the Forth Naturalist and Historian (Editorial Board) (FNH) as an informal body to promote the environment and encourage and publish contributions to the natural and social history of central Scotland. FNH has since run these symposia plus other events and published an annual journal and a number of books and pamphlets. CFSS has continued to support the symposia over the years, and its members have regularly reported on the presentations made to them and published these in the CFSS half-yearly Newsletters.

These thus provide a brief record as follows–

Symposium	Year	Theme/s	CFSS Newsletter			
			No.	Vol.	Part	Pages
1	1975	Forth Estuary and Carse, Moorlands, Man and Landscape	16	5	(4)	19-20
2	1976	Run Rigs, Flowers, Birds, Country Park	18	6	(2)	10-11
3	1977	Flanders Moss, Butterflies, Doune Muckhart	20	7	(1)	15-21
4	1978	Climate, Fish, Recreation, Haldane, Fairy Knowe broch	22	7	(3)	1, 21
5	1979	Fossils, Gartmorn, Peregrine, Devon Birds, Flight	24	8	(20	7-9
6	1980	Earthquakes, Rainfall, Nimmo Woollen Mills and	25 27	9 10	(1) (1)	5-7 31
7	1981	Howieton, L Lomond Birds, Forth, RLS ...	28	10	(2)	14
8	1982	Wildlife, Conservation, R Burns, Bronze and Iron Age sites ...	30	11	(2)	12-18
9	1983	Lochs, Culross, Battle of Stirling Bridge	32	12	(2)	18-29
10	1984	Waterpower, Sandmartins, Coal ...	34	13	(2)	11-14
11	1985	Conservation, Recreation, L Lomond, Agriculture, Aerial photography, Industrial ...	36	14	(2)	8-13
12	1986	Scenery & Geology, Cornstones ... Fisher Row, C Scotland bird watching	38	15	(2)	10-24

Addresses

Authors and Reviewers
W. R. Brackenridge, 7 The Square, Ashfield, Dunblane, FK15 0JN.
M. A. E. Browne, British Geological Survey, Murchison House, W. Mains Road, Edinburgh, EH9 3LA.
Ian Collie, Uam-Varich, Perth Road, Dunblane FK15 0BU,
G. A. Dixon, Stirling Council Archives, Unit 6, Burghmuir Estate, Stirling, FK7 7PY.
D. Grinly, 6 Grodwell Drive, Alva, FK12 5NU.
S. J. Harrison, Environmental Sciences, University of Stirling.
C. J. Henty, Psychology, University of Stirling.
Jupiter Wildlife, Wood Street, Grangemouth, FK3 8XG.
Wayne Pearce, History, University of Stirling.
Louis Stott, Creag Darach, Milton of Aberfoyle, FK8 3TD.
M. Trubridge, W. Grange House, Gribloch, Kippen, FK8 3HS.
M. van Hoek, Lauvier 20, 5061 WS, Oisterwijk, Holland.
Fiona Watson, History, University of Stirling.

Board Members – other than University
J. M. Allan, 28 Kenilworth Road, Bridge of Allan, FK9 4DU.
R. McCutcheon, The Bookshop, Spittal Street, Stirling.
K. J. H. Mackay, Hayford House, Cambusbarron, FK7 7PR.

THE FORTH NATURALIST AND HISTORIAN

A charitable body to promote Central Scotland heritage/environment (SCO 13270). Member of the Scottish Publishers Association.

The Forth Naturalist and Historian (FN&H) is a Stirling University (SU)/informal enterprise. The Editorial Board was set up in 1975 by several Stirling University and Central Regional Council staff to provide a focus for interests, activities and publications of naturalist, environmental, heritage and historical studies for the mid Scotland area.

The annual FN&H series of volumes acts as an authoritative complement and successor to the Transactions of the Stirling Field and Archaeological Society 1878-1939 – a major source of naturalist and historical studies.

Orders/enquiries to Honorary Editor L. Corbett, University of Stirling FK9 4LA or 30 Dunmar Drive, Alloa FK10 2EH, tel: (01259) 215091; fax (01786) 464994, telex 777557 SunivG; email dsm2@stirling.ac.uk. Titles here are FN&H in print, some are shared, associated or commissioned

1   AIRTHREY AND BRIDGE OF ALLAN. rev. ed. 40pp, FN&H. (0-9514147.9.8). £1.85 (p&p 70).

2   ALLOA IN DAYS OF PROSPERITY, 1830-1914. In Preparation, c120pp. (0-9506962-8-5) – Early 1997.

3   ALLOA TOWER – 1987, 40pp. Clackmannanshire Field Studies Society (CFSS). £1 (p&p 70).

4   CALATRIA. Journal of the Falkirk Local History Society. Half-yearly from Nov. 1991. £3.50 (p&p 80).

5   CENTRAL SCOTLAND – Land, Wildlife, People. 230pp. £5 (p&p £2) $8. (1-898008.00.0) (a bargain book initially £12.50).

6   DOUNE AND KILMADOCK – historical notes. M. Mackay. 126pp. £3.50 (p&p £1.20). (0.9506962.5.0)

7   DOUNE – postcards from the past, McKenzie. 40pp. 1988. (p&p 50) (0.9506962.9.3).

8   DUNBLANE – history. A. Barty. reprint by Stirling Libraries. 300pp. £15 (p&p £1.50).

9   ENCHANTMENT OF THE TROSSACHS – Fairy traditions. Louis Stott. 32pp. £2.40 (p&p 60).

10   THE FORTH NATURALIST & HISTORIAN – annual – from 1976, is supported by BP. Each volume of c124pp. has climate and bird reports for central Scotland, 6 to 8 naturalist and historical articles and book reviews and notes. Back notes at reduced prices (each) (p&p 70) – Vols 2, 3, 4, 6 at 50p; 1, 5 £2; 7-10 £1.00; 11 £2, 12 £1.50, 13 £2, 14 £4, 15 £3.50. Three 5yr List/Indexes 1-, 6-, 11-15, 50p; some papers are available as separates from Editor, e.g. Climate, Bird and Flora papers; at c5p per page, and some 20 as pamphlets. Papers/notes for publication are welcomed.

Vol 18 1995, £6 (1.898008.07.1) 140pp incl. Bathymetric Resurvey of Lake Menteith; Wintering Farmland Birds; Ochils Forestry; Thornhill 1696; Joseph Denovan Adam – animal painter (1842-96); Clan Gregor and Rannoch; Cunninghame-Graham Country; Endrick Valley Early Textile Industry; Tulliallan 1st Schoolboard; and reviews and notes.

11   LIBERTY OF THE BELL. Bothkennar Church. 1730. W B MacLaren. £2 (p&p 50).

12   THE LURE OF LOCH LOMOND – the islands and environs. McAllister. 56pp (0.9514147.6.3) Due late '96.

13   THE MAKING OF MODERN STIRLING – Lannon. 0.9506962.4.2. £4 (p&p 80).

14   MINES AND MINERALS OF THE OCHILS. CFSS/FH&H. 44pp. 1994, reprint. £1.50 (p&p 60).

15   NEWSLETTERS OF CFSS (two per year) Current issue £1, others 40p as available (p&p 60). 5 yr contents/indexes 40p each.

16   THE OCHIL HILLS – Land, Wildlife, Heritage, Walks, 60pp. (CFSS/FN&H) (0.9506962.3.4) £3.50 (p&p 80).

17   PATTERNS OF ERROR: the teacher and external authority 1581-1861 in W. Lothian, Stirling, Clacks, Fife, Kinross, by Andrew Bain, 22 Clarendon Road, Linlithgow. 1990. 230pp. for only £1.50. Pt II FROM CHURCH TO STATE 1862-72. £6.50 (p&p £1.50) both available for the author. See also Schoolboard of Tulliallan 1873-6 in FNH vol. 18.

18   RING OF WORDS – Literary Landmarks Series. L Stott – Creag Darach. (1) Stirling and Clackmannan £2.95. (2) Argyll £2.95. (3) Loch Lomond £3.95. (p&p each 70).

19   STIRLING JOURNAL INDEX. Vol. 3 1920-70 £2 + p&p £2.50 if not collectable.

20   WOOLLEN MILLS AND BUILDINGS OF THE HILLFOOTS – B Park. 180pp 1996 reprint £5 (p&p £1.50).

MAPS – LOCAL AREAS

21   GODFREY 15"/m reprints of 25"/m 1890s OS maps, folded (some available flat) at £1.85 each (p&p 50) 25 titles commissioned by FN&H – Alloa; Alva/Tullibody/Menstrie; Balfron/Killearn; Bannockburn; Bathgate; Bo'ness; Bridge of Allan; Doune/Callander; Clackmannan and Kincardine; Denny; Dollar/Muckhart; Dunblane East & West; Dunipace; Falkirk; Grangemouth; Larbert/Stenhousemuir; Linlithgow; Polmont; Stirling – 4 maps – St Ninians; Stirling North; Stirling 1896; Stirling and District; Tillicoultry. Also available – Perth, Dundee, Kilmarnock, Edinburgh, Aberdeen and Glasgow areas, and many others in Scotland, England and Wales.

NB All have historical notes or in adjoining maps e.g. for Denny see Dunipace; for Dunblane West see Dunblane East; for the four Stirling maps see Stirling 1896 and Stirling and Distirct.

22   Late arrivals – two books on Falkirk history (1) Life and Times, by I Scott 200pp and (2) Falkirk or Paradise – the battle of 1746, by G Bailey 250pp – both £9.95 published by J Donald.

Titles out of print – Clackmannanshire guide to historical sources; Muckhart; History of old Stirling; This is my town (Falkirk); Firth of Forth Wildlife.

Discount terms to trade, and societies, delivery charged for small orders. Pay on order or within 30 days, (90 at less discount) to 'Forth Naturalist and Historian' – cheques or by BACS Bank of Scotland 80-91-29 Acc 00251348.